D1084812

John W. Campbell,
COLLECTED EDITORIALS FROM *ANALOG*

. . . the inertia of the human mind and its resistance to innovation are most clearly demonstrated not, as one might expect, by the ignorant mass—which is easily swayed once its imagination is caught—but by professionals with a vested interest in tradition and in the monopoly of learning. Innovation is a twofold threat to academic mediocrities; it endangers their oracular authority, and it evokes the deeper fear that their whole laboriously constructed intellectual edifice may collapse.

ARTHUR KOESTLER, *The Sleepwalkers*

John W. Campbell,
COLLECTED EDITORIALS
FROM *ANALOG*

selected by Harry Harrison

DOUBLEDAY & COMPANY, INC.
GARDEN CITY, NEW YORK
1966

"Coincidence Day" by John Brunner, "Fighting Division" by Randall Garrett, "Overproof" by Jonathan Blake MacKenzie, "The Adventure of the Extraterrestrial" by Mack Reynolds, "Say It With Flowers" by Winston P. Sanders, "Balanced Ecology" by James H. Schmitz, reprinted by permission of the authors and the authors' agent, Scott Meredith Literary Agency, Inc.

"Countercommandment" by Patrick Meadows, reprinted by permission of the author.

"Mission 'Red Clash'" by Joe Poyer, reprinted by permission of the author.

"Computers Don't Argue" by Gordon Dickson, reprinted by permission of the author and the author's agent, Robert P. Mills Literary Agent.

INTRODUCTION

When I was fifteen years old I thought John W. Campbell was God. Since that time I have altered my views a bit—but I am sure that there must be boys that age who are today reading *Analog* with much the same emotion. While teen-age enthusiasms are a commonplace, it must be realized that a difference exists here, for this is the same magazine that Albert Einstein subscribed to, the one that Wernher von Braun had sent to him by way of Sweden during the war, so that he would not miss a single issue.

John W. Campbell became editor of *Astounding Stories* in 1937, a position that he has held ever since. He guided the metamorphosis of that garish-covered pulp magazine through a number of wonderful and intricate title changes and physical shapes, to its present form as *Analog Science Fiction/Science Fact*. Or more simply, *Analog*—or *ASF*—to its quarter of a million readers and vociferous supporters. Every issue of *ASF* since 1938 has contained an editorial by John W. Campbell. In the very early years these usually took the form of a boxed page of description of the stories in the issue or future plans for the magazine, ordinary editor-reader matters. However odd bits of information and opinion began to creep in, until all the references to the fiction were squeezed out of the editorial and formed into other departments of the magazine. The editorials took on a unique character of their own, they became Campbell Editorials, and have been the center of controversy ever since.

It would be unfair to consider these editorials in the abstract, since they are irrevocably linked with the magazine that contained them and the man who wrote them.

ASF cannot be dismissed as just another science fiction magazine. As regards its fictional content the history is very clear— the best of all the modern writers were developed in its pages, and the appearance of their stories in this magazine marked the change from pulp fiction to modern fiction. All credit must be extended to them for the maturity of their work, but at the same time due credit should be given as well to the editor for guiding their hands. None of these writers has been so small as to deny the influence of John Campbell, and the number of books that have been dedicated to him gives evidence of this. At a guess I would say there are at least thirty, a record that I am sure is unique in literature.

John W. Campbell is a born trouble-maker. The mere fact that something exists and that millions believe in it does not convince Campbell of its validity. Quite the opposite, this seems to be the point where he begins to doubt. His background appears to be ideally suited to this task, since he was introduced to physical science at the age of three, became interested in philosophy at six and read his first science fiction at the age of eight. He made himself thoroughly unpopular with other children by treating all their games and enthusiasms as problems in need of a solution. Once he had solved the problem—such as using a standard naval search pattern, a spiral moving out from the center, to wipe out the game of hide-and-seek—he lost interest and moved on to something new.

If we can thank the depression for anything, it is for blighting the career that Campbell was trained for. He went first to MIT, but graduated from Duke University where he took his degree in physics at a time when no one at all was interested in hiring physicists. His education may not have been the ideal training for the jobs he held as a car and air-conditioner salesman, but it certainly helped him to write science fiction. He had been writing—and selling—SF while still an undergraduate, and he continued to do so on an expanding scale. It was good fiction; stories written then for the pulps are still in print today—as books.

All of the parts of Campbell's work overlap and are related. First as a writer, then becoming editor of one of the magazines that published his stories. While he was editor he wrote a handful of stories and sold them to himself under a pen name. This is an accepted editorial practice, particularly when income tax payments are coming due, but Campbell did it because writers were not turning in the kind of "thought variant" stories he wanted to print. So he had to give them samples of what he was looking for. He stopped writing stories as examples as soon as he had mastered the technique of the Campbell editorial inquisition, or writer's conference. This has been likened, by writers who have experienced it, to being fed through a buzz saw or a man-sized meatgrinder. It is a painful process, I'll vouch for that, because a Campbell conversation consists almost entirely of loaded questions that demand answers. No one really likes to be forced to think. Campbell forces you. It is a heartening experience that should be part of the training of all budding SF writers, providing their hearts are in good shape and their sweat glands functioning well.

Through the years, while all of this had been going on, John Campbell was writing an editorial every month. These are idiosyncratic, personal, prejudiced, far-reaching, annoying, and sabotaging. All of these terms have been applied by readers—and far stronger ones as well. An editorial on physics always produces a flood of correspondence that appears as four or five pages of mathematical symbols in *Brass Tacks,* the letter column. The next editorial, on politics, will bring the social scientists out of the woodwork with arguments blasting, both pro and con. For almost thirty years now the Campbell editorials have produced shouts of joy and moans of pain from thousands of *ASF* readers.

Campbell is always happiest when far out on a limb, and a good number of his editorials have been prognosticative. Very often the prophecy has been right. As long ago as 1938 he predicted that atomic energy would be released, and encouraged his writers to do stories about both the atomic bomb and the peaceful uses of nuclear fission. In the mid-1940s, just after the first atomic bomb had been dropped, he looked ahead to future developments and predicted that this weapon would someday be outclassed by the hydrogen bomb. Mulling over the problems that would face the designers of this bomb, he suggested that they use the infinitely cheaper lithium hydride rather than tritium. Though a good number of atomic physicists read the magazine they did not consider using it as a textbook. They should have. A $2,000,-000,000 plant was built to produce tritium and in 1952 the first hydrogen bomb was exploded. The Russians, who did not have the facilities or techniques to manufacture tritium, found a way to make lithium hydride work instead in their hydrogen bomb. This chemical costs $12 a pound. If the Atomic Energy Commission had read the *ASF* editorials more closely they might have saved a few billion dollars.

There is no point in attempting to describe a Campbell editorial; in the following pages the reader may see for himself just what varied forms this creature takes. Neither will I claim that these are the only editorials that could be assembled in book form. Taken in their entirety they add up to a five-foot shelf of original thinking on a number of topics, and I have made a purely personal choice of those which I considered the most interesting and the most characteristic. I have called upon many people for aid, and have received it, since it appears that everyone has at least one favorite. There has been no shortage of material: at a modest estimate the editorials have totaled more than 900,000 words over the past twenty-eight years.

Inevitably, the passing of time has ruled out the inclusion of some. Many of the editorials of the late '40s and early '50s dealt with current and pending advances in atomic theory and practice. In other cases fact has caught up with editorial prediction.

Veteran readers of the magazine will look in vain for at least two topics that have been associated with the pages of *ASF;* the machine known as the Dean Drive, and that rather eccentric theory of mental aberration, Dianetics. This is not wilful censorship on my part, but has been dictated by the material. John W. Campbell never wrote an editorial advocating either of these discoveries. I will be glad to aid all those who raise a howl of agony at this bit of alarming news; you'll find the editorial about Dianetics in the May 1950 issue, and the one about the Dean Drive in the issue dated exactly ten years later, May 1960. *About* is the proper word to use since both editorials talk about the subject in question and mention briefly that an article or articles will appear on the subject. John W. Campbell did not champion either of these causes. The cause he supported—with blasts on the trumpet and salvos of artillery—was the right for controversial ideas to see print and to be considered by the authorities. That was all he ever said. His magazine printed the material, the follow-up articles, and the vitriolic correspondence.

He himself championed neither—just their right to be heard. Go ahead and look. It surprised me too.

In making the final selection I have tried to be as far-reaching as I could, including representative pieces to form as broad a spectrum of topics as possible. But in one case I must admit to personal prejudice, that is the editorial entitled *A Matter of Degree*. It concerns a characteristic of atomic reactors termed the k-factor, and how this factor might be applied to human behaviour. When I first read this it sparked a train of thought that produced a story that I titled—with great imagination—*The k-Factor*. Campbell editorials, like Campbell conversation, are stuffed with story ideas that are free for the taking. That is all they are. There is no positive feedback cycle that guarantees that the editor will buy his own idea when dolled up as a piece of fiction. It must still be a successful piece of fiction in its own right. A small army of filing cabinets could be filled with the rejects of authors who imagined otherwise.

I have grouped the editorials for easy reference, though as far as interest goes this volume can be dipped into at random, or read from back to front. The editorials were written as separate and distinct entities, and defiantly remain that way. Four of them even managed to avoid categorizing, other than being forced into the very elastic mould of being used as the closing pieces in the book. It is here that you will find the only Campbell editorial ever written about science fiction itself, *Non-Escape Literature*. In the opening group there is *Hyperinfracaniphilia*, the editorial that raised the most enthusiasm—or at least brought in the most mail.

Regular *ASF* readers who are hurt that John W. Campbell did not champion the Dean Drive or Dianetics, will be cheered by *We MUST Study Psi*, which uncompromisingly plugs for greater attention to what used to be called mental telepathy or extrasensory perception. But the backbone of the argument here is that there are incontrovertible forms of PSI that anyone can demonstrate. John Campbell is a difficult man to argue with.

In the March 1965 *Analog* he said this:

Editorially, I shall continue to try to investigate the nature of the stuffing in any suspiciously bulging shirts around. My business is directly concerned with the progress and achievement of the human race; any orthodoxy that tends to sidetrack or otherwise impede progress is interfering with my business, and I'll do what I can to sabotage them.

This is a good statement of what these editorials basically are, but it is not a complete one. It does not describe the unique twist of the Campbellian mind that sees the entire world from a different angle—and holds up a mirror that enables us to see it that way too. It leaves out the capacity to pull in apparently unrelated factors from disparate fields to generate a new picture of reality. It omits the constantly renewed enthusiasm that makes reading the editorials a pleasure.

I would like to thank Dr. Leon E. Stover for both advice and aid in uncovering copies of magazines I no longer possessed, and Kingsley Amis for suggestions and literary succor. My gratitude also to Brian W. Aldiss, Poul Anderson, James Blish, and Tom Boardman, Jr., for their assistance.

I would particularly like to thank John W. Campbell for writing the editorials and for editing the magazine that I have read with pleasure for every one of those twenty-eight years. May he continue to do so in the twenty-eight to come.

HARRY HARRISON

London   January 1966

CONTENTS

LOGIC

AN ORIGINAL POINT OF VIEW

POLITICS—A NEW LOOK

A FINAL EXAMINATION

SHAKING THE FOUNDATIONS

THE LESSON OF THALIDOMIDE

The thalidomide disaster is, of course, by no means finished; it will continue to be a disaster at least as long as any of the affected babies are living. And the lesson the human race can learn from that thalidomide disaster should go on . . . well, really, forever.

Unfortunately, I have not seen the proper lesson of the thalidomide results published anywhere; what I have seen published has, in every case, been exactly the wrong lesson.

Many thousands of years ago now, Man first learned—first of all animals—the correct lesson from being burned by fire. The lesson had to do with how you *could* handle fire; the other animals only learned to fear fire.

The importance of that difference is that they are still animals —and this is Man's world.

The basic lesson to learn from the thalidomide problem is, simply, that human beings were, are, and always will be expended in the process of learning more about the Universe we live in— and that we'd be wiser to acknowledge that, and accept it. When you do true exploration into the Unknown—some explorers are going to die. John Glenn stated very flatly that men were going to be killed in the effort to penetrate space—that he was lucky, but that deaths were inevitable.

The human race just expended several thousand babies in a battle against disease and misery; this has happened before, and we would be most wise to recognize quite clearly—as clearly as Glenn recognized his danger—that it will most certainly happen again.

And there isn't one thing we can do about it.

Human life is *not* sacred; it is expendable for cause. The Universe doesn't hold it sacred, quite obviously; if we do, we're unrealistic—which means essentially, "neurotic."

Let's take a solid, rational look at the story of thalidomide.

In the first place, Dr. Frances Kelsey acted in a whimsical, arbitrary, illogical, and unscientific manner in failing to license thalidomide for distribution in this country. Her course of action—actually, her course of inaction—was absolutely unjustifiable.

The fact that it was completely correct and right has nothing whatever to do with the question of whether or not it was logical, scientific, or justifiable. It may have been a case of pure "woman's intuition" working with illogical, but magnificent accuracy. It may have been a case of precognition—of seeing the future accurately. If either were the case, it would have been totally unscientific, illogical, indefensible . . . and right.

It might have been simply someone with a constitutional inability to make a decision who kept thalidomide off the market in the United States—one of the type who simply can't bring themselves to make a definite decision.

Such a person would have been just as helpful, in this case, as Dr. Kelsey.

Fundamentally, Dr. Kelsey had absolutely no scientific reason—no defensible justification—for not granting thalidomide a license. Her actions with respect to the ethical pharmaceutical company seeking to produce it were arbitrary, whimsical, and unjust.

All of those statements remain one hundred per cent true despite the fact that she saved hundreds, or thousands, of personal tragedies by her inaction. The only circumstance under which it could be held that her actions were logical and just are that you hold that Dr. Kelsey had clear, reliable, dependable extrasensory perception by which she perceived clearly and reliably the future facts that, at the time, were not available.

And that is, basically, why we must acknowledge and accept that the thalidomide type disaster will recur so long as human beings seek to explore for a better way of doing things.

Study the history of thalidomide briefly: It was synthesized first by a Swiss pharmaceutical firm. Tests of the new compound were made on animals, and it was found that thalidomide had *no* effects—either positive or negative. It was an "inert ingredient" so far as the animals were concerned; the substance was abandoned in 1954.

Then the West German company, Chemie Grunenthal, started further investigations on it. Their careful tests also showed that it had no pharmacological effects on animals. The only reason they persisted was that thalidomide had now acquired a "crucial experiment" importance, practically. According to the best theoretical understandings, that particular type of molecular structure *should* have sedative effect—and if thalidomide did not have any effect, the theory needed some serious reworking.

So Grunenthal tried it on human patients—on epileptics as a possible anticonvulsant. It did not act as an anticonvulsant, but did act as an excellent sleep-inducer, in human beings. It gave restful, all-night sleep without after-effects, and was remarkably safe—so safe it could be sold without prescription. It was, literally, safer than aspirin; would-be suicides have succeeded by taking sufficiently massive quantities of aspirin—but would-be suicides who tried massive doses of thalidomide simply woke up after a somewhat prolonged sleep. It was far safer than the barbiturates; Marilyn Monroe's death by barbiturates would not have succeeded, had thalidomide replaced the barbiturates as tranquilizer-sedatives.

The "goofball" addiction would not be able to replace barbiturates with thalidomide; it doesn't act that way.

Thalidomide, as of 1960, had proven itself to be by far the safest, gentlest, most nearly fool-proof sedative pharmacology had yet discovered. Even by intent, a man couldn't hurt himself with the stuff!

The situation then was that a drug which could replace the very useful, but somewhat dangerous, barbiturates had become available—a drug so safe small children could use it—and so safe small children getting into the forbidden medical cabinet wouldn't kill themselves with it.

As of late 1960, then, Dr. Kelsey's whimsical, arbitrary, and unjustified action—or inaction—was keeping from the American public a drug which could replace a definitely dangerous, definitely toxic, and somewhat habit-forming drug, the barbiturates.

Thalidomide had been tested again and again by major ethical pharmaceutical houses, had been approved for nonprescription sale by government after government, and had been widely and safely used by many millions of people all through Europe.

Dr. Kelsey was, by nit-picking and dillydallying tactics, blocking the licensing of a safe, proven, and cheap replacement for a known-to-be-somewhat-toxic drug.

Logically, that position was totally unjustifiable.

It had all the earmarks of a petty Civil Servant tyrant, fussing endlessly, delighting over the power red-tape gave . . .

At this time—say January, 1961—there was no scientific reason to doubt that thalidomide was one hundred per cent safe, and a very successful drug.

In early 1961, some reports of a polyneuritis effect due to long-continued massive dosing with thalidomide began to appear. Its symptoms were a tingling "leg's gone to sleep" sort of feeling in hands and feet; discontinuation of the thalidomide dosing cleared up the cases usually, fairly promptly.

Be it remembered that the barbiturates, which thalidomide sought to replace, were favorite suicide pills, were habit forming, and had plenty of not-so-good possibilities latent in them. Of the two, thalidomide was far and away the safer . . . *on the basis of all available data.*

But that slight tendency to peripheral neuritis when overused for long periods was the only slightest indication that thalidomide had *any* untoward effects.

Dr. Kelsey promptly used that data as a basis for more, and more elaborate nit-picking and inaction. She demanded more reams of then-unobtainable data. Her position was, at that time, for the first time, faintly logical—slightly defensible on the basis of scientifically acceptable data. But it would still be rated as poor judgment and exaggerated caution. The American pharmaceutical company seeking to market thalidomide, naturally, was growing quite impatient with the unjustifiable and indefensible, and thoroughly illogical delaying tactics that were blocking them.

Neither "womanly intuition" nor "a strong hunch" has ever been held to constitute adequate grounds for governmental rulings, and precognition isn't considered to exist.

A German doctor was the first to suspect thalidomide of its actual disastrous characteristic—and it was November 15, 1961 that he first warned the Grunenthal company that he suspected their thalidomide preparation of being responsible for the "seal-baby" epidemic then appearing in Germany. At this time his data was still too scanty for him to make a definite statement. His first public discussion—"public" in the sense that it was made to an official medical group meeting in Germany—was on November 20, 1961—and then he was not in a position to state that thalidomide was responsible, but merely to say he strongly suspected a certain drug, which he did not name.

At this point in the development of the problem, data came in very rapidly; within a month thalidomide's danger was clearly recognized . . . and only then did Dr. Kelsey's inaction on the licensing application become absolutely defensible.

That the United States was saved from this disaster was not —repeat *not*—due to any scientific, logical, reasonable or even justifiable action. It was due to those totally indefensible and anathematized things, "a hunch" and/or "woman's intuition."

That Dr. Kelsey's hunch was one hundred per cent valid has nothing whatever to do with whether it was logical; for all I can know, she may have perfect and reliable trans-temporal clairvoyance, so that, in 1960, she was reading the medical reports published in late 1961, and basing her decisions very logically on that trans-temporal data.

The essential point is that *no possible logical method can prevent another thalidomide-like disaster.*

If the Federal Drug Administration can recruit a staff of expert crystal-ball gazers, tea-leaf readers and Tarot-card shufflers, it might be possible for the F.D.A. to rule correctly on all future drug licensing applications. Nothing short of genuine precognition can prevent such disasters completely.

Let's imagine the most completely and perfectly conservative, cautious, experimental program we can think of that will still allow some progress in medicine.

Suppose we require the following steps:

1. Careful and complete animal testing before any human testing is permitted.

2. A two-year test period on a very limited number of human

beings so that, if there is some joker in the deck, it will afflict only a small number of people at worst.

3. A second two-year test on a larger number of patients—say about ten thousand people.

4. Released as a prescription medication only for another two-year period, so that close observation can be maintained.

Sounds reasonable and conservative? And yet there are a few known instances where a substance has a time-bomb effect so delayed that as much as *fifteen years* may elapse before the deadly effect appears. Beryllium dust poisoning is one example of a time-delay bomb. If you inhale BeO dust, it definitely won't hurt you a bit right away—and cases of a fifteen-year delay have been reported.

Inasmuch as we now have pretty good indication that genetic information is carried as a chemical code on protein molecules, it's conceivable that a substance might be discovered which affected only the genetic cells of unborn babies. That one would first begin to show its effects about eighteen years after it went into use. (Yes, some girls affected by the stuff would start having babies at thirteen or so . . . but not until a large number of affected individuals had babies would the statistical numbers become large enough for credibility and identification.)

So even a very, very cautious five-year system wouldn't catch all the time-bomb drugs.

And we *can't* run a fifty-year program like that! If someone finds a cancer cure today, will the world wait until our grandchildren demonstrate that it has no hidden menace, do you think?

And as to that cautious, two-year-plus-two-year program . . . thalidomide would have been licensed with flying colors!

Test 1 is the animal test. Thalidomide proved completely harmless—in fact completely ineffective!—to the usual laboratory animals. (Since the blowup, it's been found that enormous doses of thalidomide will not make a rabbit sleep . . . but will cause a pregnant rabbit to produce abnormal young. Equally massive doses of barbiturates don't do that; they kill the rabbit. It wouldn't have indicated anything to the investigators except that thalidomide was safer than barbiturates! And it has now been discovered that, for reasons so far known only to God, thalidomide *does* make horses sleep! But who uses horses as "convenient laboratory animals for testing new drugs"? And why should they; horses are herbivores, with a metabolism quite a long way from Man's. Monkeys are expensive—and they don't really match Man.)

Test 2—trying it on a small group of patients first.

Now the first slight indication that thalidomide could have some bad side-effects was that neuritis business. It results from prolonged overuse of the drug.

The doctors administering the first test-use of the new drug would, of course, regulate it carefully. There would be no long-continued overuse under their administration—and therefore thalidomide wouldn't have produced any neuritis.

On that first, limited-sample test, there would be an inevitable, human tendency to avoid pregnant young women as test subjects for so experimental a drug.

Result: thalidomide would have checked in as one hundred per cent safe and effective.

The final two-year test was several thousand people. On this one we don't have to guess; we've got the statistics.

During the time thalidomide was being considered by the Federal Drug Administration for licensing in this country, selected physicians in the United States were sent supplies of the drug for experimental use.

Under this program, 15,904 people are known to have taken the pills. Certainly that's a good-sized second-level testing group for our proposed hyper-cautious test system.

Of those nearly 16,000 people, about 1 in 5—3,272—were women of child-bearing age, and 207 of them were pregnant at the time.

There were no abnormal babies born, and no cases of polyneuritis reported.

Thalidomide passed the cautious tests with flying colors.

Now the abnormalities that thalidomide does cause are some kind of misdirection of the normal growth-forces of the foetus. The abnormalities are of a type that was well known to medicine long before thalidomide came along—abnormal babies have been produced for all the years the human race has existed, remember.

Suppose that in our test, some women did bear abnormal babies. Say three of them were abnormal, and lived. (A goodly number of the thalidomide-distorted babies died within hours. It doesn't *only* affect arms and legs; thalidomide can mix up the internal organs as though they had been stirred with a spoon.)

So . . . ? So what? Aren't a certain number of abnormal babies appearing all the time anyway? And with all this atomic-bomb testing going on . . . and this woman was examined repeatedly by X ray during pregnancy . . . and remember that in the normal course of nine months of living, she will have taken dozens of other drugs, been exposed to uncountable other environmental influences, perhaps been in a minor automobile accident . . .

Not until the drug is "tested" on literally millions of human beings will it be possible to get sufficiently numerous statistical samplings to be able to get significant results. Toss a coin three times, and it may come heads every time. This proves coins fall heads-up when tossed?

Another drug was introduced for experimental testing some years ago. The physicians who got it were told to check their experimental patients carefully for possibilities of damage to liver, stomach and/or kidneys, the expected possible undesirable side-effects of the drug. Practically no such damage was found—the drug was effective, and only in the very exceptional patient caused sufficient liver, stomach or kidney reaction to indicate it should be discontinued.

Only it caused blindness.

The reaction was frequent and severe enough to make the drug absolutely impossible as a medicament—and was totally unexpected. It had not caused any such reaction in any of the experimental animals.

No—the lesson of thalidomide is quite simple.

So long as human beings hope to make progress in control of disease and misery, some people will be lost in the exploration of the unknown.

There is no way to prevent that. There is no possible system of tests that can avoid it—only minimize the risk.

We could, of course, simply stop trying new drugs at all. The animals never did try the pain and the risk of fire. They're still animals, too.

JANUARY 1963

SEGREGATION

I am strongly in favor of rigidly segregated schools, and I believe that you are, in fact, in agreement with me—that it is absolutely necessary for the continuation of the United States in the terms we know it that our schools be segregated considerably more rigidly than they are today.

The liberals and do-gooders and those with special advantages to be gained have brought about changes in our schools, in our entire educational system, that is becoming an acute menace to America—and the Supreme Court decision such as the *Brown vs. Board of Education* case (the basic case in the integration cases in the southern schools during the last decade) was a serious mistake.

In the above statements, *I am not referring to racial segregation*, however. I'm referring instead to the overlooked and enormously critical problem of *segregation by individual student ability*.

The reason why the Negro segregation case, *Brown vs. Board of Education*, is so unfortunately tied up in the mess, is that it has been the basis for suits that do, in fact, make for improper integration of students of completely different, and noncompatible inherent learning ability.

The tremendous fuss and furore going on throughout the nation over Negro integration—racial integration in general—has so concentrated attention on that one completely unimportant factor that the really important factors of inherent individual differences have been violently suppressed.

And when I say that racial difference is a "completely unimportant factor," I mean that—and that proposition is, in actuality, what the most rabid integrationist NAACP member holds, too. That *racial differences* are not important.

The trouble underlying all this boiling-over racism is a complicated mass of snarled-up thinking, and horribly ill-defined terms. No one of the groups most violently involved in the dispute has done a half-way honest job of analysis of the facts involved; each is acting on violently emotional Doctrines, Dogmas, and Principles. And none of those doctrines, dogmas or principles has been defined well enough, by any one of the contending groups, to make sense of their own position, or that of any of the other groups.

The result is bad enough with respect to general living conditions; its effect on the educational system is not merely bad; it's disastrous.

I quite deliberately started off this editorial by making a statement that was practically certain to arouse strong antipathy in many readers—for the specific purpose of making it clear that you, too, have been suckered into falling for a propagandist's definition of "segregation" to such an extent that it's almost impossible today to read a statement without reacting to that propaganda—value. Just what does "segregation" mean? What's "a segregated school"?

Any non-co-educational school is segregated by sex.

We have rigidly segregated washrooms all over this country, not just in the South. Segregated by sex. And don't get sloppy in your thinking and say, "But that's *natural!* How else could it be?" Remember that neither the highly civilized Japanese, nor the Finns consider it "natural."

I noticed in a Savannah, Georgia, paper the other day that a Negro and a white woman were contending for some elective office in a local campaign. A century ago, both contenders would "naturally" have been barred.

"Segregation" means Negro-vs.-white, does it? For Pete's sake, friend, *please* straighten up your thinking and your terminology enough so that rational communication, outside of the propaganda-broadside method, is possible!

"To segregate" means nothing more than separation of a mixed collection into groups having determinably different characteristics. Like segregating ripe fruit from green fruit.

The *Brown vs. Board of Education* case didn't make segregation, as such, illegal; it made segregation *on the basis of race alone* illegal. It's still perfectly legal to have a school rigidly segregated on the basis of sex, of course. Or segregated on the basis of blindness, or on the basis of requiring that all registrants have graduate degrees before being admitted.

The trouble with the *Brown vs. Board of Education* decision stems not from law, but from libertarian assumptions that were built into that case, and from "scientific evidence" that seems to be definitely inadequate, and which has been attacked as actually fraudulent.

Propaganda can produce some results that are straight out of fantasy, fairy stories, and the *Alice* books. Propaganda has the wonderful characteristic that Adolf Hitler—one of history's most expert and effective propagandists—very clearly stated; a lie told often and loud enough will overcome truth. Particularly if a considerable number of people would *like* to have it be true. Then the Big Lie becomes That Which Should Be True Whether It Is Or Not . . . and dedicated believers in the lie arise to *make* it true.

Among the Big Lies of current cultural propaganda are a set of meaningless noises that sound like important, deeply philosophical Truths—because they strike many people as being desirable. Among examples are:

"Everyone has a right to his own opinion, so long as it doesn't interfere with anyone else."

"All men are equal."

"What goes up must come down."

"There's nothing new under the Sun."

You can extend that list of philosophical-sounding noises almost as far as the trajectory of Mariner II . . . which went up, isn't going to come down, and is a new satellite of the Sun. They all *sound* important, and they can be quoted with the philosophical-authoritative pompousness appropriate at various times when they support your dearly-beloved position, so they tend to seem as though they ought to be true whether they are or not, so they just must be true.

That business about opinions, now; what does the stupid thing mean? That you are free to think anything you want to, no matter how insane it may be, so long as no one else has the slightest interest in what you think. So long as your ideas aren't of any importance whatever, to anyone else, and don't influence your behavior in any degree that bothers anyone else, you can think anything you darned well like, and nobody will give a damn.

Note carefully that if you decide you want to be a hermit, however, that interferes with other people's opinions; they have the opinion you should work for a living, for instance, so under that doctrine of no-interference, you do *not* have a right to the opinion "I want to be a hermit" since it does interfere with someone else.

The problem is, was, and always will be "What rights exist between people when opinions *do* interfere?" Obviously there's no problem so long as opinions *don't* clash! That silly-season statement about non-interfering opinions is, of course, a perfectly sound proposition to answer a problem that never exists.

So . . . let's have some thinking about what to do when opinions do seriously, definitely, interfere; that is the real, human problem.

As to "all men are equal," that bit of nonsense is equally meaningless. Can you tell me one, single respect in which men are equal? Equal before God? Not if you accept any of the religions which hold that God segregates sinners from saints! And offhand I can't think of any religion which holds that God (or the Gods) don't judge, evaluate, and make distinctions between men.

"Equal before the Law?" Oh . . . yeah . . . ? You mean a man of IQ 50 is held to have the same responsibilities and duties as a man of IQ 150? That all men must pay equal taxes? That some men, who are licensed doctors, don't have, under the law, special rights and special duties? That attorneys don't have special rights, privileges and duties before the law? (An attorney can't be summoned to jury duty.)

The difficulty is that God decided for reasons not clear to us that men should not be equal—and He created them with inherent differences. And men cannot undo that fact. But doctrinaires can sure try!

The deadly part of it is that men can make unequal individuals equal by one method; they can cripple the strong, until the best has been sabotaged down to the level of the worst. They can take away the "unfair advantage" of the intelligent by crippling his abilities, punishing his achievements, and destroying his powers, until he is less competent than the normal. In times past, Kings and Tyrants held that they held the "power of Life and Death"; no King or Tyrant in all history has ever held the power of Life. They have, however, held the power of death and destruction and crippling.

The doctrinaire—the Tyrant Liberal—today, holds that ancient power of Death and Destruction—and that is his weapon to achieve what he Just Knows is Right and Just—to make all men equal, despite God's unfairness in making some men more capable than others.

In the current cultural situation, it's been made easy to see that intransigent southern segregationists are seeking to suppress the competent individual Negro, to make him less-than-equal to the not-so-bright whites.

What's not so easy to see in the fog of emotionalism, is that the libertarians and do-gooders are seeking to suppress the unusually competent individual *of any race* for the achievement of their doctrinal ideal of equality.

Here's where the trouble comes: a school system that "rewards" the more-competent student with more work, harder tasks—and no increased privilege, no increased status or desirable reward is, in fact, effectively punishing his display of ability. Suppose the reward for superior achievement in the classroom—finishing the assigned tasks more quickly—was being given the "privilege" of scrubbing the floors, polishing the windows, and tending the school grounds. Or running errands for the students who were slower and hadn't finished their assignments yet.

Who would, obviously, be the "second-class citizens" of that school? The students who were so stupid they acted bright, of course!

Such a system of punishment-for-extra-achievement is almost inevitable in a school not segregated by intelligence and ability. For any individual, a certain level of problem represents a stimulating challenge; a higher level of difficulty becomes an overwhelming task that defeats him, discourages, and drives him to withdraw his effort. A too-low level of task simply bores him, and he will seek more interesting tasks, or seek to do the assigned task in some more stimulating manner.

The extra-competent, in a randomly selected class, will present to the normal and subnormal the fact that the work can be done with ease, quickly, and simply—that it can be done offhand as a sort of game. They slap the dullards in the face with the clear fact that children their own age—not just teachers!—can do that work offhand. The honors student who finally gets around to doing the term paper the last weekend before it's due . . . and earns an A+ for one afternoon's work, while the rest of the class spent four to six weeks researching and rewriting to get a passable paper.

The super-competent, too, can earn the enmity of the teacher in a normal school. Karl Frederick Gauss, for instance, could have expected to be punished for one trick he pulled. In a grade-school arithmetic class, when he was about seven, the teacher had told the class to add all the numbers from 1 to 100—this being a good way to keep the children usefully busy while the teacher got some of his own work done.

Young Karl Frederick, however, was up with his answer in about two minutes. Young Karl Frederick had not added all the numbers from 1 to 100; he'd developed for himself the formula for the sum of a series of numbers, and instead of *working* the problem, had *solved* it—in a matter of seconds. His answer was, of course, absolutely correct—which took the teacher some minutes to check.

But young Gauss was lucky beyond expectation; that teacher was wise. He recommended Gauss to the local Duke as a proper subject for patronage; Gauss' family was poor and could not have given him an education.

In an educational system dedicated to the problem of producing equality—such a teacher is out of place. That teacher was not producing equality; by seeing that Gauss got special reward for remarkable ability, the teacher exaggerated an already existant inequality.

Unsegregated schools are injurious to the subnormal and the

geniuses alike. The subnormal, discouraged and overwhelmed by the equality-for-all problems presented them, withdraw from the hopeless effort of education, and achieve far less than their already limited potentials. An equality-for-all school does not allow the less-talented to develop the maximum of the abilities they do have.

And it does not allow the abnormally competent to develop their high talents. It's stupid to expect a normal school teacher, herself oriented to everybody-ought-to-be-equal and nobody-has-a-right-to-special-advantages, to welcome the idea of some ten-year-old who can outthink her, penetrate the errors of her logic, call her on sloppy statements, and do a job of research in the library such that the teacher is forced to acknowledge her lack of information on her subject.

But . . . now we run into a very nasty aspect of the *Brown vs. Board of Education* decision, and its subsequent development.

Recently, several towns in New Jersey have been forced to "integrate" their "segregated" schools; the basis of the NAACP suit was that one school had a ninety per cent Negro enrollment, and the other a ninety per cent white enrollment. This, they contended, constituted *de facto* racial segregation.

That particular town had a population distribution by areas that made that the natural result. The NAACP was, of course, just as hotly against that sort of population distribution—but that wasn't the legal point in the case.

It was decided that because of the fact that registration did not show a proportional representation by race, that therefore there was *de facto* segregation.

That is not a logical or valid conclusion.

It certainly falls in the class of "data insufficient for the conclusion proposed."

Yet that is an accepted proposition—and that proposition alone would be enough to cause great difficulty in setting up segregated-by-student-ability schools.

There is a never rigorously proven assumption that's thrown around in all racial arguments that all races show the *same* distribution curve of intelligence and ability. *That has not been proven.*

There's adequate evidence to the contrary, available from a number of lines of analysis. First, in a normal distribution curve, the number of individuals—in a statistically significant large population—in any one range gives the scale of the curve; from the curve, then, the number in any other range can be predicted. That is, if we find one hundred twenty-five high geniuses at IQ 180, knowing the shape of the distribution curve, we can predict how many individuals of IQ 100 there will be in this population, et cetera.

Now *if* all races have the same distribution curve, then knowing the population of the group, we can predict how many super-high geniuses will appear.

Something seems to be wrong; some gears slipped somewhere. The assumptions don't match the facts. The Caucasian race has produced super-high-geniuses by the dozen in the last five thousand years; the Oriental race has, also. The Negro race has not. And it's the super-high geniuses, not the ordinary, or run-of-the-mill geniuses, that lift a people from one level of civilization to another. The Industrial Revolution, for example, depended on a number of super-high-geniuses, backed up by a corps of high geniuses, working with an army of geniuses. The super-high-geniuses are never educated; they educate themselves, because there's no one around to teach them. Who could teach Abraham Lincoln, for instance? Who could teach Leonardo da Vinci? Certainly Newton did have formal schooling—but the schools he attended were attended by a lot of other young men, and there does not seem to have been any sudden flood of Newtons coming from them. "Educational opportunities" never exist anywhere for the super-high-geniuses.

The fact that the Caucasian race has produced more super-high-geniuses in the last five thousand years suggests that the distribution curve for the Caucasian race does not in fact match that of other races.

I'm not talking about text-book type psychological-testing geniuses here; I'm talking about the individual of super-high, unmatchable pragmatic achievement. Anyone who says that Newton wasn't a super-high genius is off his rocker.

These super-high geniuses produced achievement that promoted the survival ability and adaptability of their race. Pasteur made it possible for men to adapt to disease-saturated areas by intellectual act that had, theretofore, been uninhabitable save by the slow process of genetic selection and evolution. This achievement made men more adaptable.

You don't have to rate those achievements in any special cultural terms—increased adaptability is the pay-off coin in the evolution of living things! The great chemists made it possible for human beings to eat rocks, drink petroleum, and be nourished. The race is more adaptable because of their genius—and that is a positive gain in absolute, not merely cultural, terms!

There is an indication, then, that the white race may in actual fact have a distribution curve that does not match that of the Negro.

Note the important factor in citing the super-high geniuses; *educational opportunities play no part whatever in the development of any super-high genius*. There is not, never was, and never can be anywhere or anywhen, in any land or race, a school for educating super-high geniuses. The thing that characterize the super-high genius is his ability to self-educate to totally new and hitherto undiscovered horizons. They are *always* self-made men. Newton needed calculus to solve his gravitational problems—and he lacked the educational opportunity. Nobody ever taught him calculus. So he had to invent it.

Karl Frederick Gauss wasn't taught to find the sum of a series of numbers; he invented it.

The super-high genius, then, is an indicator of a people that is not dependent on educational opportunities—because the opportunities never exist for any of them!

And there is other and more ordinary evidence that proportional representation of races is not the right answer.

To carry out a really wide-spread, long-continued, massive testing program, involving tens of thousands of individuals, and keeping track of them for some years, is an expensive proposition. The money for such a program is not easy to come by.

Most of the discussions of racial distribution of intelligence has been based on pretty limited samples, or quite inadequate testing.

The old WWI Army Alpha intelligence test results, for instance, are still among the few massive test-score result records, and are still being used simply because they're available.

The schools system of Savannah, Georgia, since 1954, has carried out a massive testing program. Standard IQ tests, Mental maturity tests, and scholastic achievement tests were given to all students in the Savannah school system, and punched-card records kept for nine years, and the results computer analyzed.

The results showed that, at beginning grade-school level, the Negro children had a fifteen per cent crossover with the white children's scores. (That is, fifteen per cent of the Negro children scored at or above the level of the norm of the white children.) At high school level, the crossover had dropped to two per cent.

Now let's just consider for a moment the emotional fireworks that would result from setting up a school system that was strictly, honestly segregated purely by individual student competence, simply using those figures for discussion purposes.

Assume that we have a city with a fifty-fifty distribution of Negro and white population, and that we set up two school systems; one for those above the white norm, and one for those below that norm.

The Doctrine, Dogma and Principles boys will be out for Hell and hallelujah. *Both* sides will be. The intransigent white segregationists will be shrieking in defense of their violated Principle of the Color Bar. Their howls of rage will be exceeded, however, by the violent anguish of the NAACP, at the destruction of their Principle of Proportional Representation. But those howls won't be audible above the far louder and angrier screams of the parents of the children who have been officially designated "incompetent; second-class citizen." The whites will, of course, be peculiarly violent about that, because that's precisely what they've been afraid of for a century or so—the admission that some Negroes are superior to some whites.

The acute psychological pain resulting from such a system will be very real indeed—and will, curiously, bring the underlying principles of the *Brown vs. Board of Education* case into the thing in a sort of back-handed manner!

The basis for the Supreme Court's decision in *Brown vs. Board of Education* was testimony by a psychologist that segregation imposed psychological hurt on the rejected Negro children.

The Court's decision, then, was, in effect, that it was illegal to cause someone psychological hurt.

So we now have a very interesting question that needs resolution; if it hurts an individual to be told the truth, is it illegal— unconstitutional—to make him aware of that truth? Of course, that general idea is part of our present cultural philosophy—the poor, misguided sadist shouldn't be made unhappy about his misdeeds. And this poor, disturbed child shouldn't get severe punishment just because he slugged the corner cigar-store owner, stole his money, and set fire to his place. It isn't *nice* to hurt people; it should *never* be done, because it isn't Kind and Good and Brotherly.

So . . . if it's unconstitutional to cause psychological discomfort, we can't have segregated-by-intelligence schools; they'll make some people extremely unhappy.

And if segregation-by student-ability turns out—as we have reason to expect—to produce a system in which proportional representation of races does not exist . . . why, we can't have segregation by ability for that reason either.

Then, of course, the liberal-do-gooder group just *knows* everybody should be equal, whether they are or not, and they know that schools are intended to produce equality, not education anyway.

All in all, practically everybody has motivations for wanting the present unsegregated school system to continue in American education.

The problem the United States faces is very simple: We have developed the highest standard of living the world has ever known, by developing the potentials of technology—of applied education.

But this process has certain penalties; it is, in a very real sense, a specialization in the evolutionary sense. Now we have developed this technology, we cannot do without it. The population which we are, today, supporting in luxury could not be supported, even at a subsistence level, without technology. Those wheat surpluses that are troubling the nation aren't due to the innate fertility of the soil; they're due to applied agricultural science—to biochemistry and genetic science and soil technology.

The civilization that we in America know today is based on and dependent on high-level technology—and that of course means high-level technicians.

Inasmuch as men are not equal, not all boys can be trained to be technicians—and it is the sheerest insanity, the sheerest refusal to face reality, to believe for a moment that all children can be so trained. Only those children originally gifted with the required potentials can have those potentials developed into the needed abilities.

Now an educational system dedicated to the proposition that if all men aren't equal, we're gonna teach 'em to be, can only equalize men downward—it has the power of death, but not the power of life. The power of Life is reserved to God—and any people that mistakes itself for a collective form of Diety is doomed.

Today, despite long and loud campaigns for more young scientists, our technical schools are getting fewer applicants than they were before—fewer registrants from an increasing population!

The medical profession is having serious troubles, too. The doctors in most communities now are working fifty hours a week routinely, and sixty hours a week commonly—and they do not do so because they get paid time and a half for overtime. I mentioned that doctors represent a group of men who are not equal before the law; their inequality seems to be resented. Certainly the public is making life miserable for them. A doctor is required by law to stop and render aid if he passes a highway accident—and today they hate to do so, because it quite commonly means a malpractice suit. The man the doctor saves by his emergency treatment is quite apt to sue for a few hundred thousand dollars; you see everybody knows that doctors carry insurance, and you can always get somebody to get on the stand and prove that his hindsight is better than the sued doctor's foresight, and testify that if such and such had been done, maybe the patient wouldn't have the scars he has.

In the Great American Lottery—suing after an accident—it pays better to sue the doctor that saved your life than the man who nearly killed you; doctors carry bigger insurance policies.

And besides, them there rich doctors oughta pay fer things; nobody's got any business being rich, cause people are equal, ain't they?

Medical schools for some reason are having difficulty getting enough registrants—even when they rather desperately lower their standards for admittance. Anybody who chooses medicine as a career today has to be pretty much of a peculiar type; his reward for saving lives is malpractice suits. He's required to work fifty to sixty hours a week . . .

Then we have another interesting technological problem. It's the problem of interconnections and interactions among communicating units. The telephone people ran into it long ago; when you double the number of telephone subscribers, you don't just double the number of switching connections required—it increases exponentially. The original system was handled by human operators; as it became more complex, machine-switching became essential. As of now, to handle the telephone switching problem in New York City, even if *all* employable women in the service area were employed as operators, the system would be unable to function.

As intercommunication increases, the problem of switching increases drastically.

That's happening in the problem of business organization. The number of interacting businesses in this country today is so great that the number of business executives required is also straining the limits of our capacity. But the "switching" involved there is decision-making, judgment-application—which is the factor machines can't handle.

It takes human beings of trained potential—men trained to think, think accurately and quickly.

A breakdown in any one of those three areas—science technology, medical technology or business technology—will mean a collapse that will be most interesting to historians of the future.

It will be the first time in history that a culture collapsed because of the failure of the educational system.

Never before has a culture been dependent on efficient education, so it has never before been possible.

It won't be at all interesting to those involved. Old-timers will be talking about the good old happy days of the early 1930s, when all we had to worry about was a Depression.

If the Supreme Court finds that the Constitution forbids segregated schools that make the incompetent unhappy—then it's time to start a campaign for a constitutional amendment that holds that Truth is never illegal, no matter how painful it may be.

OCTOBER 1963

"YOU'RE PROBABLY DEAD . . ."

1 Statistics show that over 98 per cent of all individuals born are now dead.

2 Therefore you're probably dead now.

Well . . . ? It's perfectly logical isn't it?

"HYPERINFRACANIPHILIA"

You won't find that term in any dictionary that I know of, nor any textbook on psychology, but I think it's a term needed to describe one of America's most widespread neurotic tendencies. It means "having a neurotic and excessive fondness for the underdog," without having the slightest interest in finding out why he is in the infra position.

For example, let's consider the poor people that great "war against poverty" is supposed to help.

Now I've been looking into the situation of a group of people in one area on the fringe of that Appalachia region who have some very tough conditions to contend with. Their region is very backward, very underdeveloped, and astonishingly underindustrialized. The people in that area aren't able to buy tractors, and have to do all their farming—most of them are farmers—entirely by their own hard work. They don't even have electric power, and hence no electric lights or power-driven equipment. Of course that also means no radio or television for relief, during the long evenings, from the hard work of their living. Their children can't go to the public schools. They don't have automobiles to get around in, but travel by horse and buggy. These poor people . . .

Oh, you know about the Amish people, huh? You've seen their beautiful, lush farms, their big, sturdy barns and their spotlessly-kept homes? Well, I know they almost universally have good, fat bank accounts, but aren't they "poor people" in that they don't have the conveniences of modern life?

Well, what *do* you mean by "poor people"? Perhaps you mean "poor" in the sense of "genetically incompetent, lacking the qualities of intelligence, ambition, self-respect and determination necessary to adequate accomplishment." Certainly the Amish aren't "poor people" in that sense; what they have proven a man —and this does, of course, mean he has to be a *man*, not a whimpering bum—can accomplish with his own muscles, using intelligence, determination, and willingness to work adequately demonstrates that they aren't "poor" genetically.

The next time some victim of hyperinfracaniphilia tells you how this, that or the other group or individual "didn't have a proper chance," it may be appropriate to compare the situation of the named group or individual with the standard Pennsylvania Dutch situation. What would have happened to an Amish family dropped into the situation? Would they be living in a leaky shack, in ragged clothes, unwashed, ill-fed, and penniless?

Take a run through the areas full of those "poor people," look at the tumbling shacks, slovenly men and women, the TV antennas decorating every ill-patched roof, the fairly late-model automobile standing in the ruts across the grassless lawn—and not so much as a well-tended vegetable garden in the empty acres of land. They've got electricity, TV, a car . . . and are ill-clothed, ill-fed, and ill-housed in an area where there's acres of unused land.

Oh, it's poor land, that won't raise good crops?

You can't teach those people anything useful, so it would be useless to import some Scottish farmers, men accustomed to farming barren, treeless hillsides, with soil leached of practically all plant nutrient by the nearly ceaseless rains, with a growing season shortened by the fact that they're as far north as Hudson's Bay—and men *not* accustomed to whining about their hard lot.

You won't see any sheep on the hillsides in Appalachia, either, nor appropriate breeds of cattle. Sheep yield wool as well as meat, which, with a bit of effort, can be turned into excellent clothing—without the need for a major industrial complex. Ask your nearest librarian.

There is a great deal of talk, too, about the selfishness of the better-off people, and the hyperinfracaniphilia type insists that we should help these poor people.

It is certainly true that those poor people are completely unselfish. No one can accuse them of having done anything for themselves, and isn't it held that the mark of selfishness is that you do things for your own interest?

How can you help people who are so unselfish that they practi-

cally never do anything for themselves? Of course you can rebuild their shacks, make new clothes for them, and guarantee
them a life-time supply of quick-frozen TV dinners . . . but the
new clothes are no better than the old. They don't keep themselves clean, repair their own careless rips and burns, or adjust
size to match growing children. The new houses aren't a bit better than the old; their windows break, and the wind lifts shingles
just the same, and the poor people living in them know they've
been cheated.

The great advantage of nudity is that the animal or human
skin is self-repairing—and arranged to encourage the wearer to
avoid carelessness in the matter of rips and burns—reasonably
self-cleaning, and self-adjusting to the changes in the wearer's
size and/or shape.

The advantage of free forest living is that trees—although they
do constitute a somewhat leaky roof—are self-replacing, self-
repairing, and if one falls down, there are always others you can
move under. There's no work involved.

These completely unselfish poor people, however, are not really
interested in forest living, because of the lack of adequate TV
entertainment, and the unsatisfactory food supply.

It is *not* a matter of poor education, either. Let's get that nonsense out of the way. Abraham Lincoln had a darned sight less in
the way of economic, social, or educational opportunities than
the poor people of Appalachia have. And, moreover, millionaire
scions graduating from Harvard turn out to be just as totally
unselfish—they won't do a thing for themselves—as the worst of
Appalachia's people.

The best way to express the problem, I think, is to recognize
that no matter how you heat-treat or work a piece of cast iron,
you're not going to make a usable spring out of it. There are,
however, a wide variety of steel alloys which, given different,
but appropriate heat and work treatments, will yield springs. And
there are alloys which make highly effective springs in a straight
as-cast condition. In analogy, you can't educate a piece of cast
iron—and there are some alloys that don't need to be educated;
they have the wanted characteristics built in. Plenty of individuals

have proven resoundingly that a man who has that education-absorption characteristic gets his education even if it's clearly impossible. The Negroes who complain so bitterly about poor educational opportunities, for instance, should consider George Washington Carver's life a bit more carefully; he, like Abraham Lincoln, saw to it he got an education, despite the near-impossibility of the conditions he faced. These were selfish men indeed; they worked hard doing something for themselves, instead of whimpering to have others do it for them.

Michael Faraday did it in science. How about "Joseph Conrad," an essentially uneducated Polish seaman who decided to write in a language—English—other than his native tongue because his works would have a wider market.

Certainly there will always be a great majority of individuals who don't have that tremendous level of built-in drive and determination—people who can, with adequate educational opportunity become useful, self-supporting and self-respecting citizens who, without that external help, would gravitate to the "unselfish" category of those who don't do things for themselves. The alloys that make powerful and highly elastic springs in the as-cast condition are few, highly expensive, and seldom used, too; practically all springs are the result of starting with a good, workable alloy, and applying heat and work treatments—educating an educable alloy.

But to hold that *all* alloys are educable to the same degree is absolute nonsense. What school was it that turned out Einstein? Did they operate that school only once, for one individual, for some reason?

Now one of the most important aspects of education for the low-grade student is convincing him that he damned well better learn as much as he himself is able to—because if he doesn't work at it, he's going to pay for his laziness in future misery and discomfort.

The hyperinfracaniphiliac however, is busy assuring the inferior human alloy individuals that they should, indeed, be unselfish —and let other people support them. They are repeatedly assured that they don't have to exert any extra effort, because they will be assured equal rewards in our society, even if they don't work.

Why shouldn't the "drop-out" drop out? Go ahead, sucker—work and get all that education, and get a job. So what does it get you, huh? The drop-out gets welfare, relief, unemployment payments, et cetera, and antipoverty supplies, and has three hundred sixty-five holidays a year, and a lot more orators defending him, discussing his good, unselfish attitude than you have defending yours!

What pressure is there to make the lower end of the ability scale even try to develop himself? He could, with some real effort, achieve considerable development of his limited potentials, and achieve self-respect—by being selfish, and doing something for himself. Instead, encouraged by all those hyperinfracaniphiliacs, he relaxes, stops making even minimal efforts, and achieves self-respect by listening to the TV orators explaining how he's just as good as anyone else because he's human, and he has just as much rights because he's a citizen—he got born here, which, fortunately, takes no effort whatever on his part.

Why *should* this individual of low inherent ability try to make the most of his limited potentials?

You, poor sucker, were born not only with potentials, but with a drive to use them. (Or you wouldn't have achieved an educational level that makes this magazine interesting to you.) You're stuck with being selfish, and working for your own development. He isn't—so why should he, since he will be honored, respected, and fed without working?

The hyperinfracaniphiliacs are establishing a situation with the interesting characteristic that those individuals born with relatively low potentials are strongly encouraged to *not* develop what talents they have! If he doesn't try at all, he can't fail—and he will retain self-respect because he is assured that he is Human and a Citizen and An Underprivileged Man to whom The Society Owes Something.

He doesn't try, therefore doesn't fail; if he did make a real effort, and fully recognized that his abilities were limited, he wouldn't have the comforting self-respect of accepting that he is, really, Just As Good As Any Other Man. He couldn't feel so wholeheartedly that he was an Oppressed Victim of Society and that his poverty was not his own fault.

Poverty doesn't make poor people; poor people make poverty. The test is quite simple; consider what has happened when a different type, or group of people has been put in a precisely similar circumstance.

It isn't slums that make slum-dwellers; slum-dwellers are a type of people who, when they move into an area, make slums.

You can not solve that problem by giving poor people goods and money; they'll make poverty of it. You can't end slums by moving the slum-dwellers into new, clean, well-built housing— but you can end the slum by moving non-slum-dwellers into the dirty, rat-and-louse infested, run-down buildings of the slum. Rat traps are cheap; DDT is readily available, soap, water, scrub brushes, paint and paint brushes are readily come by. Most slum areas have heavy unemployment; how come all those unemployed people can see nothing to do in their dirty, dilapidated and unpainted slum homes? How come they keep complaining about it so loudly, and demanding that somebody should fix it for them?

Because they're so unselfish, of course.

FEBRUARY 1965

BREAKTHROUGH IN PSYCHOLOGY!

Life magazine, a few months ago, announced a startling break-through discovery in psychology made at a California research clinic. Some psychologists there had come up with the amazing discovery that punishment—hurting a child deliberately, for cause —actually helps children to grow into sounder personalities.

This startling discovery comes a little late, however. It seems to have been anticipated some hundreds of millions of years ago, when mammals first developed from the reptilian predecessors.

The psychological doctrine of "Mustn't punish a child; it might hurt his precious little ego" derives strictly from the reptilian division of the animal kingdom. They never punish their young. They're apt to eat them, of course, if they encounter them—but there's nothing of intent to hurt; it's simple hunger that motivates them.

The greatest of the mammalian inventions was not live birth— some of the earliest sharks gave birth to live young. The mammals invented reward and punishment for their young—guidance. Punishment was the great mammalian invention—a substitute for being eaten alive when the individual made a mistake.

Of course, the Freudian notion that "sex is the only instinct" explains the young animal's tendency to seek the mother on the basis of an Oedipus Complex, overlooking the fact that young mammals are thermotropic and hungry and could—just possibly —have certain other instinctual drives.

After some 150 megayears, it's reasonable to suppose that young mammals have a built-in expectation of being guided by punishment and reward—and that failure to offer that guidance introduces stresses into the young mammal. Certainly failure to give reward—affection and attention—is known to have a literally lethal effect on human babies. It's been proven that babies given every objective necessity of life—food, warmth, cleanliness, ex-cellent medical care—have a near one hundred per cent death rate if they get *only* the objective necessities. But a baby born in a cold drizzle, deprived of shelter, under-nourished by a half-starved mother, survives and grows—if that half-starved mother strives to care for it and keep it.

Isn't it reasonable to assume that if one half of the ancient instinctual pattern is necessary, the other might be, too? The worst kind of lie is a half-truth; if you are entering a strange environment, and I tell you only what you should do, and omit all warnings of danger, things you should not do, I could arrange very neatly to have you kill yourself.

The psychological dictum of "Punishment is bad; it is mere desire for vengeance," has, of course, seeped over into the sociology of our times. The trite and stupid argument that punishing a criminal does no good, because it's mere vengeance, and capital punishment is useless because, after all, it has never stopped murder, takes off happily from that psychological crackpotism. The argument that punishment doesn't stop crime is equivalent to saying: "We shouldn't try to stop drunken driving, because even when we have laws against it, drunks still drive."

It spreads and digs in deeper, and comes up with the wonderful idea that the young criminal shouldn't be clouted for his vandalism; he should be gently scolded, and encouraged to do better.

There's the old saying that: "Power corrupts; absolute power corrupts absolutely." It's a false statement. Power has almost no correlation with corruption—they're completely independent variables. If it were true, then it would necessarily follow that God Almighty was the ultimate in corruption.

The true statement is *"Immunity corrupts; absolute immunity corrupts absolutely."*

The current clamor about "police brutality" stems from the basic idea that individuals should be free of punishment—i.e., *that criminals should be immune.*

The automatic consequence of that increasing degree of immunity is the observed increasing corruption, the increasing vandalism of JDs, which recently expressed itself in several hundred million dollar damages in Los Angeles. The City of the Angels turned up with some red-hot demons on the loose.

It's worth noting that the total amount of property damage the

Los Angeles vandals did to that city probably exceeded the total of property destruction the Vandals did to the city of Rome when they sacked it.

The "brutal" actions of police consist of punishing criminal behavior.

We have problems—very serious and pressing problems—concerned with social relationships in our culture. And you do not solve problems by denying that they can possibly really exist, or by denying that their actual cause could possibly be the cause. If your car stalls because the ignition wire is broken, filling the gas tank won't restart it. Cleaning the carburetor won't get it going. Putting in a new battery doesn't help. You'll eventually have to repair the ignition wire, one way or another. You might kid yourself the wire wasn't really at fault by installing a whole new ignition system—but one way or another you're going to fix that wire before it runs again.

The immensely destructive riots in Los Angeles, Chicago, and other cities were not, at the start, primarily racial—they were mainly the young barbarians against the "police brutality" of authority that refused to grant them the absolute immunity they wanted.

Once started, it snowballed, and the older barbarians joined in happily. The true Vandal spirit was manifested in their delight in setting fires that burned out whole blocks of property. They were revolting in search of "freedom now" in one sense—freedom to do what they damned well pleased, with no punishment threats, with total immunity.

Ninety per cent of the Thoughtless Liberals' excuses for the JD, and for the arrogant defiance of law by many of the Negro "Civil Rights" groups, has been based on arguments about how terrible it is to grow up in a ghetto—that such crowding and dirty conditions inescapably breed crime. That it isn't the fault, or the responsibility of the colored people, but the natural consequence of such conditions.

That, my friends, is absolutely one hundred per cent obvious nonsense. It is totally wrong, and strictly propaganda guff.

The simplest evidence is directly available in almost all of our great cities. It isn't a matter of how terrible it is to be physically marked by skin-color, either.

Take a look at the other "ghetto" of colored people you'll find in almost every major U.S. city. A ghetto densely populated by colored people who didn't have a Chinaman's chance, after they were imported to this country for heavy labor at starvation wages, for domestic servants, and the like. People marked by differently shaped features and by skin color, demeaned and rejected, crowded now into city ghettos.

No Civil Rights movements have sought to better their lot. Their schools have not been integrated—and until pretty recently, the White culture didn't offer their children much schooling anyway.

But the Chinese sections of our large cities, just as densely crowded as the Negro sections, will never be confused with them. In New York City, for instance, Chinatown doesn't remotely resemble Harlem. It's one of the cleanest sections of the city—and it has the lowest crime rate of any section. The crime rate there is lower than it is for the fancy Park Avenue apartment district. And it's clean and crime-free *not* through the special efforts of the City; the colored people who live there see to it.

I have heard of no complaints whatever concerning "police brutality" coming from Chinese. (They discipline their own children, and don't wait for the police to try to do it for them.)

It is absolute nonsense to say that a ghetto *automatically* produces dirt and criminals. The Chinese prove that that's a false notion.

There's been a lot of talk about civilian review boards to check on "police brutality." I have a suggestion. Since the accusations of brutality come to such a large extent from the Negroes, and are directed against White police, let's have a board dominated by racially neutral arbiters—Chinese. I have a strong feeling that the complainants would howl in dismay at the idea; the Chinese have the lowest crime rate in the city, which means a solidly established respect for law, order, and discipline—for nonimmunity. They do *not* hold that punishment is "mere vengeance," and practice the alternative proposition, that punishment is necessary to guidance.

Another standard proposition about ghettos is that they automatically discourage individuals living in them from seeking or even accepting education.

The term "ghetto" originated with the Jewish districts in European cities. These sections were, therefore, characterized by high crime rates, excessive juvenile delinquency, and general rejection of education?

The number of Chinese who have somehow managed to become major scientists—despite the claimed impossibility of achievement starting in a ghetto, with a colored skin—is worthy of note.

The extent to which men from the Jewish ghettos somehow overcame that "impossible" problem of education to become a major force in every intellectual field of endeavor suggests that it isn't ghetto-living that prevents achievement.

And integrated schools obviously aren't necessary for achievement, either; the Jews were, for centuries, denied entry to nearly all the great schools of Europe—and yet somehow managed to turn out great intellectual leaders for all those centuries.

If you insist on blaming the carburetor for the failure of the car to start, when it's the ignition wire—*you can not solve the problem.*

If you insist that it's segregation and ghettos that cause the problem the Negro faces—*you can not solve that problem.*

Because that's not where the problem lies.

It's not skin color; the Chinese had that problem, and their young people are decent, law-abiding, self-disciplined youngsters who are well-educated and are achieving in many fields.

It's not ghettos and segregated schools. The Jews proved that didn't matter, centuries ago.

It's not that a history of being rejected and demeaned leaves a stamp that can't be overcome. The Irish, Jews and Chinese all encountered the problem. So did the Italians. So did practically every ethnic group that moved into this continent. (Including the original Scotch-English settlers, who were very lethally rejected by the then-dominant majority.)

The problem seems to lie in this question: What's the difference between "punishment" and "torture"?

Unfortunately, that problem lies in the subjective, not the objective, realm. Each involves the objective fact of pain deliberately inflicted. But whether that pain reacts on the individual personality as "punishment" or "torture" depends entirely *on the recipient's interpretation.* A flogging rates as "torture" to the individual who cannot accept that he did anything wrong—and as "punishment" to an individual who recognizes his own choice and actions earned what he's getting.

If an individual holds "This is cruel and vicious vengeance this enemy is inflicting on me," he will undergo torture, and seek to avenge it in turn.

Another individual, with a different orientation, in the same situation may hold, "Well, they caught me at it, dammit. I knew they might—so I get a flogging." This doesn't mean that he agrees with his punishers—but that he acknowledges that they are punishing, not torturing, him. That doesn't keep him from continuing to be a rebel—but it does mean that he doesn't see himself as the victim of cruel and vengeful and wicked foes. He doesn't pity himself.

Now an individual oriented to the idea that punishment is *always* evil and is *always* mere vengeance—*cannot be punished.* He can only be tortured. To him, the police using force to restrain his vandalism are "brutally" interfering with his Natural Right To Immunity—they are torturing him by frustrating his desire to see that building go up in flames, to loot that liquor store, to smash the windows and grab those radio and TV sets. To him, any force used to restrain his unlimited freedom to do what he wants is torture and brutality.

Because—face it!—any discipline is painful. There are three kinds of discipline: Universe Discipline, Other People Discipline, and Self-discipline. But they're all painful. Stick your finger in boiling water, and you get Universe Discipline. A child who's slapped away from sticking his finger in a live electric socket is getting Other People Discipline. When he gets older, he'll keep his own fingers out of the high-voltage wiring—Self-discipline. But each kind is painful, for each is an imposed frustration of a desire, which is psychological or emotional pain.

The police have as their function the imposition of discipline on those who lack self-discipline. They rescue children who've fallen in the pond, or got stuck in pipes, or ran into the street and got hit by cars. They arrest burglars, rapists, and murderers. Their business is to supply the Other People Discipline required by those who lack Self-discipline.

To one who denies that discipline should exist, this is torture. It's deliberately inflicted pain—emotional pain of frustration at the very least. Therefore, the police are clearly being brutal; their brutality is inherent in the fact of their deliberately frustrating the non-self-disciplined individual's desires.

All of which orientation stems from that lovely piece of crack-pottery the psychologists introduced: "Punishment is always bad; it's mere desire for vengeance, and harmful to the child's ego."

The Chinese have a five-thousand-year old traditon of discipline. So do the Jews. They could, and did, live sanely and peacefully in the ghettos, in the close-packed living where every individual is constantly rubbing against every other.

The Irish, when they first came over here, didn't have that tradition. The Irish created America's first slums, and a reputation for being a brawling, undependable, dirty, ignorant people. It took them a couple of generations, but they started by disciplining each other, and wound up learning how to live as ambitious, but self-disciplined people.

The Chinese have, also, an ancient tradition of "Face"—of the importance of reputation. The Chinese felt strongly that the behavior of any Chinese was a reflection on the reputation—on the Face—of all Chinese. (Madison Avenue's taken over the idea and calls it "Image.") Wherefore, every Chinese felt that the behavior and earned reputation of every other Chinese was his personal and direct concern. If one Chinese were a crook, a criminal, slovenly and lazy—why, it impaired the "Face" of other Chinese, by indicating that Chinese were such undesirables. If one Chinese were a cheat—it impaired the reputation, the Face, of other Chinese. Wherefore the other Chinese took steps to see that the cheat stopped damaging *their* Face.

Today, a New York businessman knows he can trust a Chinese businessman to meet his debts, and to deal honestly. If, for some reason, the Chinese does not meet his debts, one of the Chinese Societies will pay them in full for him. The Chinese Society will then deal with the defaulter. The reputation of the Chinese has been protected—and if the reason for default was an honest one, the defaulter will be aided in re-establishing himself. If he defaulted by reason of cheating, measures will be taken so that he does not have any desire whatever to repeat.

The brawling, slovenly, shiftless Irish were disciplined in a basically similar manner by their fellow Irish who, like the Chinese, felt that what any Irishman did was a reflection on all Irish.

Both the Chinese idea of Face, and the Irishman's feeling that he himself would be judged by the behavior of every other Irishman, rest on an absolutely one hundred per cent valid mechanism.

The simplest way to express it is in terms of what I call the "Elsa mechanism," in honor of Elsa, the Lioness. Many of you have, I'm sure, read the two delightful books about "Elsa"—"Born Free" and "Living Free," the biography of a wild African lioness who was raised from orphaned cubhood by a pair of white African game wardens. Elsa, as a full-grown lioness, was friendly, gentle, trustworthy, and fully co-operative with human beings. She was playful, but careful to recognize her own strength and weight. If you read those books, you'll learn how warmly affectionate and genuinely friendly an African lioness can be.

So the next time you're walking across the African veldt, and see a full-grown lioness come bounding toward you—what will you do?

Unless you're insane, you'll raise your rifle and do your best to drop the three hundred pound beast before she reaches you.

Of course, if it happened to be Elsa, happily bounding toward you in friendly greeting, that would be a cruel injustice.

It would be a case of an individual suffering gross injustice because of the reputation—well earned!—of the statistical group, Adult Lionesses, of which she was a member.

In other words, the necessity of real-world statistics will force any sane individual to react to the most probable situation—and the most probable situation is that a powerful carnivore is attacking with motivation of converting you to manburgers.

Statistically speaking, the Negroes lack self-discipline. Suppressing the publication of crime statistics does not change those statistics. The fact that some individuals are brilliant, highly ethical, thoroughly self-disciplined gentlemen in the finest sense of the word—does not negate the validity of the Elsa Mechanism. Those individuals will suffer gross injustice—because of the reputation their group has earned.

That injustice to individuals will, moreover, continue indefinitely, no matter what laws may be passed. Prohibition had a better chance of stopping the consumption of alcohol than a law has of stopping the statistically based reactions of human individuals.

When lack of self-discipline—revolt against any and all discipline—explodes into a vandal group sacking a major city, the loss of Face involved can not be repaired by passing a new law saying we shouldn't notice it.

If the National Association for the Advancement of Colored People wants to truly advance the Negroes—they might learn from an older, wiser people, and study the Chinese methods. Or the younger and more ebullient Irish, who solved the same problem, in the same basic way.

The Negro must discipline the Negro. So long as the Negro leaves the problems of discipline up to the Whites, the Negro will not be self-disciplined, and will feel that he is a victim of Other People Discipline, and Other People Frustration. He'll feel that, because he truly will be—forever and ever, world without end, *until he himself takes over the job*.

The Chinese and the Irish were right; what any member of a group does, *does* reflect on every other member, whether that other member likes it or not.

If a White group imposes discipline, the disciplined individual will inevitably have a strong tendency to feel that the aliens are imposing cruel torture. If a Negro society imposes discipline, it will come far closer to being accepted as punishment and guidance.

The deep and simple basic of the problem is—*the Whites can not solve this problem, no matter what they do*. Because *anything* they do is necessarily wrong.

Only the Negro himself can solve it—because it must be solved by *self*-discipline, and *self*-respect, and *self*-help.

The ones who suffer the greatest injustice now are those fine individual Negro men and women who, because of that Elsa Mechanism, are denied the acceptance their individual personalities merit. It's tough—but it is just as inevitable and inescapable as any other law of statistics. The individual Negro who can't stand the slovenly, violent, thieving ways of his Negro neighbors naturally wants to move to a better disciplined neighborhood.

But . . . the individuals in the better-disciplined neighborhood are inescapably going to react to the Elsa Mechanism, and identify him with the Negro neighbors that he himself wants to escape.

In seeking to move away from their neighborhood, he is trying to do what he so condemns—relegating his undesirable neighbors to a ghetto, geographically removed from himself.

Man-made legislation, seeking to contravene a law of Nature, can at the very best be futile. The Elsa Mechanism is based on the laws of statistics. Trying to change it by passing laws is about equivalent to decreeing that, henceforth, the value of π shall be 3.0000. . . .

Maybe somewhere . . . but not in this Universe!

DECEMBER 1965

THE DESTINY OF MAN

ARITHMETIC AND EMPIRE

It was van Vogt's story "Storm" that started me thinking on the problem; this item would have appeared last month had it not been that the announcement of this new size became necessary. The problem is simple in statement—the governmental set-up for maintaining peace and order in a galactic empire.

At present, all theories of how planets are formed are lying in ruins. (It's interesting that, even before the discovery of the extra-solar planets, the various stellar-collision theories had been mathematically proven wrong; 61 Cygni C simply confirmed the fact.) We haven't any idea how planets come about, but *every star which we have been able to observe minutely enough to make the detection of a planet possible has shown planets.* I think it's fair to set up an hypothesis on the basis that all stars have planets; many stars have habitable worlds. Four hundred million planets capable of supporting human life, within this galaxy, is not stretching possibilities anywhere near the limits.

Then, given a fast interstellar drive, and, say five thousand years of time, what sort of human population might the galaxy develop? When it comes to population increase, rabbits and guinea pigs have a reputation as experts; the reputation is somewhat undeserved—they simply have short generations. Man can do a very fine job of increasing the population when conditions warrant it, and there's some time allowed.

This planet, under present conditions, has a population of about two billions. With improved methods of producing food—you've perhaps noticed that item about making a meat-flavored, meatlike food from yeast, ammonia and sugar?—it could support some fifty billions without discomfort. Since a planet habitable for human kind will, of necessity, be Earthlike, an average population per planet of one billion would be conservative.

That gives the tidy total of four hundred million billion people. Like the number of light-waves in a mile, the number doesn't have much emotional meaning—it remains a "4," which we can understand, followed by a string of zeros which quickly cease to mean anything real or understandable.

But this part of it does become understandable. Such an empire would have to have a home-rule governmental system, with local area governments in each city, up through continent governments, world governments, and system governments. Van Vogt suggested in "Storm" that some central government would be essential to keep individual planets, systems, sectors, and quadrants from warring amongst themselves. It seems reasonable. Let's see what sort of affair that would be.

I don't believe that the United States Federal government could be operated effectively by one hundred thirty men—including the whole set-up from President down through and including the Army, Navy and Post Office clerks. One civil servant per million people is impossibly small, percentagewise, to be effective. That's a figure that must be expanded.

But our galactic empire government must, then, have more than that microscopic percentage of one-in-a-million, must have more than an impossibly scant *four hundred billion* Federal employees.

Perhaps, if Earth were made one solidly built-up capital city-world, supported by the microscopic taxes collected from the individuals of the empire, by the goods shipped in from other, producing worlds, this one planet could serve as the empire's governing world. Otherwise, it would take some two hundred planets to support the government's functionaries.

Incidentally, a congress made up of representatives each of whom represented a billion individuals would be a more populous affair than the North American continent now is—twice over! To have a representative body of manageable size, each legislator would have to represent some million billion people.

The one-in-a-million figure of governmental employees is certainly too small; there will be some compromise figure between our present-day over-high percentage of government workers—after all, the problem of governing populations of more than one hundred million people democratically is less than fifty years old —and that too-small figure.

The availability of really fast communications will aid a lot *too.* As long as human nature remains roughly comparable to what it is today, a face-to-face, person-to-person conference will continue to be more solidly, definitely effective—and it takes time to go from point to point. Since most governmental conferring is within the capitol, fast communications—say van Vogt's trick walls— would help fewer people to accomplish more. But all this deals only with the central government. How many people would be engaged in *all* governmental work in an empire of 400,000,000,- 000,000,000 people, including town, city, county, district, continent, world, stellar-system, sector, quadrant and galactic governments?

Galactic empire has been glibly considered fairly frequently in science-fiction. But—has anyone any workable suggestions for a galactic government?

NOVEMBER 1943

NOTE FOR CHEMISTS

The American Chemical Society is holding its Seventy-fifth Anniversary Meeting in New York this September, beginning Labor Day. Those seventy-five years in review are more than mildly impressive; the 1876 model chemical science was basically something that Priestly and Lavoisier could have understood readily. But a modern technical session, with discussion of angstrom unit spacings between atoms, the molecular resonances, and the intricacies of enzyme and catalytic action would be a totally foreign language.

Foreign as the modern material would be to those old fathers of the science, the discussions planned on the impact of science—chemistry in particular—on civilization would be just as foreign to the chemists of seventy-five years ago.

In 1876, the primary effort of chemistry was to *extract from Nature the desired materials.* The background assumption of chemistry at that time—a basic philosophy so deeply assumed that it was not expressed, did not need to be stated—was the proposition that chemistry's business was to find in Nature, and extract in purified form, the materials needed, the ready-made molecules that industry required. Rubber from trees, metals from ores, drugs from plants.

The emphasis has changed vastly in that three-quarters of a century—less than one lifetime. The natural products, today, are extracted, and studied—usually, however, on a microchemical basis. A one-tenth milligram sample is adequate for many researches. Once the natural substance has been isolated and studied, the effort, instead of concentrating on improved methods of extraction, is directed toward synthesis, and towards synthesis of a more desirable similar material. Nature has a certain slight edge on chemical industry in producing useful materials—living things have had some 2,000,000,000 years to experiment. But it still seems highly improbable that the material 2,000,000,000 years of living-experimenting on the part of the hevea tree and its ancestral forms developed for wound-healing is necessarily the best of all possible materials for automobile tires.

The sheep developed, through hundreds of millions of years, a fibrous material, wool, as an effective clothing material. But it seems somewhat improbable that it can be the best possible material for Man's needs. For one thing, the sheep has a perfect solution to the problem of wool shrinkage; just don't wash it, and keep it well oiled with lanolin to protect it against rain. That works just fine—and of course a sheep doesn't mind smelling like a wet sheep.

So much of modern chemistry's effort has been directed at taking *atoms* rather than *molecules* from natural sources, or taking molecular fragments from natural sources, and recombining them to totally new synthetics designed specifically for Man's uses. No animal or plant form ever attempted to handle the problem of containing one hundred per cent H_2SO_4; it is reasonable to suppose, therefore, that a synthetic, rather than a natural product would be needed for the job.

No living metabolism here on Earth is able to handle the exceedingly stable carbon-fluorine bond in any but the most tentative fashion; organic compounds containing fluorine are, as a consequence, practically unknown. But chemical industry, with the high-energy processes available to technical machinery, can handle even such powerful bonds—and produce materials like teflon which are totally immune to corrosion.

The past seventy-five years has been a period of change from the business of extraction-from-Nature to the business of synthesizing totally new chemical systems—compounds like polystyrene plastic do not exist in Nature, yet polystyrene has become one of the cheapest, most widely used, and most satisfactory product-materials. Everything from delicate electronic parts—polystyrene is one of the world's best insulating materials—to cookie jars—polystyrene is cheap, easily molded, attractive in appearance, relatively rugged, and easily cleaned—are being made from it.

But the next three-quarters of a century . . . ? What will be the direction of development?

My private guesstimate:

The beginnings of the new developments are, I think, now in sight. Polystyrene-like materials, required in ton-lots, basically simple, repetitive molecule structures, are ideal for machine production, for purely mechanical synthesis. But the swing away from Nature can go too far—and I suspect it has.

Ecology is the study of the economy of living things; the interrelationships and interdependencies of life forms. All living things constitute a planetary organism, in a sense. Man sprang from the living forms of Earth; he is still a part of the system. In the development of organisms, living cells learned to specialize, to take on special functions, producing substances not intended for their own use, but for the use of the rest of the organism—the adrenal gland, the Islets of Langerhans, the bone marrow that produces cells that live only to produce needed corpses, the red blood cells.

Penicillin is produced by a certain type of mold—but penicillin today is produced by a specially mutated strain that is being fitted into the ecology of Man; the mold is a successful mutation because, in the presence of Man's industry, that is a survival characteristic. The modern cow is a similar evolutionary freak; the dairy cow's characteristics are survival characteristics only in the presence of Man. The modern strains of beef cattle, like red blood cells, live only to produce useful corpses. The modern strains of apple trees are similar examples; their gigantic seed pods produce seeds that are never planted, and never grow; the type is propagated by grafting.

The overall evolutionary mechanism is that *Man is creating a planetary organism in which animal forms and plant forms cooperate in mutual survival, instead of individual survival.* The liver cells of an animal are incapable of surviving alone, as their remote, ancestral forms did. Man is in process of creating a world-organism of life forms that are similarly incapable of independent survival.

And the chemist is playing a major role in that slow organization; DDT, 2-4-D, many of the sprays and medications that have been synthesized and extracted are playing a role in building that interdependency.

The next step, however, is for the chemist, in his role of biochemist, to start consciously evolving strains of living things to produce the complex compounds he wants. It is easier to produce complex organic molecules that are not simple repetitive patterns, like the synthetic polymers, by biological processes. It is also a fairly simple problem—in its basic theory—to develop, by forced evolution, a biological mechanism that produces the desired substance.

In the past seventy-five years, we have learned techniques for producing what we want synthetically; it seems to me that the next step is to produce the living organism that produces what we want.

That's a legitimate activity for a life form, too!

SEPTEMBER 1951

SPACE FOR INDUSTRY

It has been more or less assumed that when Man gets going well enough in spaceflight technology, the planets will be opened for development—that the future pioneers, future investment opportunities, will be in the development of Mars, Venus, the Moon, and, later, planets of other stars.

Maybe, eventually, those developments will come. But . . . it looks to me, now, as though we've neglected a major bet.

I think the first major development of industry based on space technology will not be on another planet—but in space itself. I believe that the first major use of space technology will be the development of a huge heavy-industry complex floating permanently in space, somewhere between Mars and the asteroid belt.

In the first place, we're never going to get any engineering use of space until we get something enormously better than rockets. (And every indication now is that we already have something that means rockets never will be used for any major space work. Tests so far made confirm that the gadget described in the December editorial does in fact break Newton's laws of motion; it provides thrust without counterthrust.)

We can, therefore, drop rockets from consideration; they're inherently hopeless as an industrial tool. They're enormously less efficient as transportation than is a helicopter—and nobody expects to use helicopters as the backbone of a major industrial transportation system.

So *any* engineering development of space implies a non-rocket space-drive. Something that can lift and haul tons with the practical economic efficiency of a heavy truck, at least. Even nuclear rockets couldn't do that; the reaction-mass problem requires that even a nuclear rocket start with a gargantuan load of mass solely intended to be discarded *en route*.

So: assume some form of true space-drive. A modified skyhook or an antigravity gadget—anything. It's a space-truck—not a delicate and hyper-expensive rocket. It can carry tons, and work for years.

Now; do we develop Mars and/or Venus?

Why should we?

The thing human beings use and need most are metals, energy, and food. It's a dead-certain bet that no Terrestrial food plant will grow economically on either Mars or Venus . . . except in closed-environment systems. Metals on those planets might be available in quantities; let's assume that Mars is red because it's a solid chunk of native iron that's rusted on the surface to a depth of six inches.

Who wants it? Why haul iron out of Mars' gravity field . . . when it's floating free in the asteroid belts? If we're going to have to grow our food in a closed-environment system any time we get off Earth . . . why not do it where null-gravity makes building the closed environment cheap, quick, and easy?

And while Terran life forms may not do well on those planets . . . the local life forms might do very well indeed living on us. Why bother fighting them off? In a space-city, there would be only those things which we selected for inclusion.

And energy?

Heavy industry has always developed where three things were available; cheap raw materials, easy access to markets, and cheap energy supplies. In pre-industrial times, that cheap energy supply naturally meant cheap fuel for muscles, whether animal or human. Somewhat later, it meant water-power, and now it means fuels.

The current direction of research efforts is to achieve a controlled hydrogen fusion reaction, so that the energy needs of growing industry can be met.

In space, that problem is already solved. The Sun's been doing it for billions of years—and the only reason we can't use it here on Earth is that the cost of the structure needed to concentrate sunlight is too great.

So let's set up Asteroid Steel Company's No. 7 plant. It's in orbit around the Sun about one hundred million miles outside of Mars' orbit. Conveniently close—within one hundred or two hundred miles—are floating in the same orbit a dozen energy collectors. They don't last long—a few months or so—but they're cheap and easy to make. A few hundred pounds of synthetics are mixed, and while they're copolymerizing, the sticky mass is inflated with a few gallons of water vapor. In an hour, the process is complete, and a horny-looking film of plastic has been formed into a bubble half a mile in diameter. A man goes in through the bubble wall after it's set, places a thermite bomb in the middle, and retires. A few seconds later, the bubble has been converted to a spherical mirror. A little more manipulation, and at a cost of perhaps one thousand dollars total, two half-mile diameter mirrors have been constructed, located, and faced toward the Sun. A little equipment has to be laced onto them to keep them from being blown out into outer space by the pressure of the solar rays they're reflecting, and to keep them pointed most advantageously.

The beam—poorly focused though it is—of one of these solar mirrors can slice up an asteroid in one pass. Shove the asteroid in toward the beam, stand back, and catch it on the other side. So it's half a mile thick, itself? So what? A few passes, and the nickel-steel directly under that mirror-beam boils off into space. Power's cheap; we've got a no-cost hydrogen-fusion reactor giving all the energy we can possibly use—and collectors that cost almost nothing.

The steel—it's high-grade nickel-steel; other metals available by simply distilling in vacuum, of course!—once cut to manageable sizes can be rolled, forged, formed, et cetera, in the heavy machinery of Plant No. 7. The plant was, of course, constructed of the cheap local metal; only a nucleus of precision machine tools had to be hauled up from Earth. And those are long since worn out and discarded from Plant No. 1.

The plant itself has a few power mirrors to provide the electrical energy needed. After all, with the free fusion-reactor hanging right out there, nobody's going to go to the trouble and risk of installing a nuclear power plant.

Plants for food, of course, need light—and they'll get just exactly as much as they can best use. So the direct light's a little weak out there? Aluminized plastic film costs almost nothing per square yard.

And the third factor for heavy industrial development is, of course, easy access to market? How easy can it get! It's a downhill pull all the way to *any* place on Earth! Whatever the system of space-drive developed, it's almost certain to allow some form of "dynamic braking"—and it's usually easier to get rid of energy than to get it. From the asteroids to the surface of the Earth you're going down hill all the way—first down the slope of the solar gravitational field, then down Earth's.

Spot delivery of steel by the megaton, anywhere whatever on Earth's surface, at exactly the same low cost follows. There's easy access to *all* markets from space!

Meanwhile Solar Chemicals Corporation will have their plants scattered somewhat differently. Landing on Jupiter is, of course, impossible for human beings—but it's fairly easy to fall into an eccentric orbit that grazes the outer atmosphere of the planet. That wouldn't cost anything in the way of power. Depending on the type of space-drive—antigravity or some form of bootstraps lifter—ships would take different approaches to the problem.

The problem, of course, is that Jupiter's atmosphere is one stupendous mass of organic chemicals raw materials—methane, ammonia, and hydrogen. And, probably, more water in the form of dust in that air, than we now realize.

In any case, if Jupiter doesn't supply oxygen from water, the stony asteroids do—as silicates. And Saturn's rings, it's been suggested, are largely ice particles.

The solar mirrors are less efficient at Jupiter's distance, of course —but Solar Chemicals doesn't need to melt down planetoids. Their power demands are more modest.

With Jupiter's atmosphere to draw on, it seems unlikely that Man will run short of hydrocarbon supplies in the next few megayears. And there's always Saturn, Uranus and Neptune in reserve . . .

We're only beginning to understand the potentialities of plasmas and plasmoids—of magnetohydrodynamics and what can be done with exceedingly hot gases in magnetic fields under near-vacuum conditions. Space is the place to learn something about those things—and one of the things we've already learned from our rocket probes is that the immediate vicinity of magnetized planets is exceedingly dangerous.

Open space might prove to be somewhat healthier than we now realize. And if there are some difficulties—generating our own, homegrown magnetic fields isn't an impossibly difficult matter. Particularly when we've got nickel-steel by the megaton to work with! And it is not, remember, necessary to build our space plants —it might prove wiser to carve them, instead.

The meteorites that reach Earth are, of course, almost entirely composed of common silicates and nickel-iron. However, the Earth is also, to the best of current belief, composed almost entirely of those materials. Nevertheless there's quite a tonnage of copper, silver, lead, tantalum, titanium, tungsten, molybdenum and other metals around here. And, presumably, in the asteroids.

Silicate meteors being common, we can expect effectively unlimited quantities of raw material for glassy materials in space. On Earth, vacuum distillation is scarcely a practicable method of separating the components of a rocky ore; in space, however, vacuum distillation is far more economical than processing in various water solutions. On Earth, high-energy processes are expensive; solution processes relatively cheap. In space, with the energy of a star to play with, solution processes will be used rarely—and whole new concepts of high-energy-level chemistry will be invented. Jupiter's atmosphere will supply plenty of low-cost carbon for constructing graphite processing equipment.

We can, effectively, make our own solar flares—our own sunspot vortices—by injecting gas into the focused beam of a half-mile mirror, traveling not across, but *along* the beam. The light-pressure effects, alone, should yield a jet of gas at high velocity equivalent to several tens of thousands of degrees.

There's every inducement for heavy-industry development in space.

And against that—what have the planets to offer?

Earth, of course, is a unique situation; we evolved to fit this environment. The planets do have open skies, instead of walls, and natural gravity, rather than a constant whirling. They are, and Earth in particular will remain, where men want to live.

Sure . . . and men today want to live on a country estate, with acres of rolling hills and running streams and forest land, with horses and dogs around.

That urge is so strong that, at least around the New York Metropolitan area, anywhere within seventy-five miles of the city, they can sell a structure that an Iowa farmer would consider a pretty cramped hencoop for forty-five hundred dollars, as a "summer home." All it needs is a pond renamed Lake Gitchiegoomie within a mile or so.

Man, you ought to see the beautiful, uncluttered landscapes in Western Ireland! Lakes that *aren't* ponds, and not even one house on them. They don't have to have water-police to handle the traffic jam of boats on a one by three mile "lake" there.

Only . . . who can afford commuting from New York to Ireland?

Well, there's one sure thing about the space-cities. They won't have the smog problem.

APRIL 1960

THE WONDER OF SCIENCE

NO COPYING ALLOWED

The proposition involving the science-fiction hero who captures the enemy device, brings it home, copies it and puts it into production is being abandoned in modern stories. But the actual difficulty of such a problem is always interesting and worthy of consideration. Only recently has Earth's own technology reached the point where such copying is not possible; today it is definitely impossible in a large field of devices.

Let's first consider this situation: Time: About 1920. Place: An American Army Air Base. Action: High overhead a small airplane tears across the sky with a high, thin whistle. Ground observers, after tracking it for a minute or so—during which time it has passed out of sight—report incredulously that it was doing between nine hundred fifty and one thousand miles per hour. It circles back, slows abruptly as the whistle dies out, and makes a hot, deadstick landing. Investigators reach the cornfield where it landed, and find it ninety percent intact—and one hundred percent impossible. Swept-back wings, no tail, automatic control equipment of incredibly advanced design, are all understandable in so far as function intended goes. But the metal alloys used make no sense to the metallurgists when they go to work on them. The "engine," moreover, is simply, starkly insane. The only indication of anything that might remotely be considered an engine is a single, open tube—really open; open at both ends. But the empty fuel tank had tubes leading into some sort of small jets in that pipe. The athodyd being unheard of in 1920, the thing is senseless. Filling the fuel tanks simply causes a hot fire that must be extinguished quickly to prevent burning out the tube. The fact that this is a guided missile intended for launching from a four-hundred-mile-an-hour bomber makes the situation a little difficult for the 1920 technologists; the athodyd won't start functioning below two hundred fifty m.p.h., and nothing on Earth could reach that speed in 1920.

Meanwhile, the Signal Corps experts are going equally chittery trying to figure out the controls. First off, the plane's markings were clearly an advanced United States Army design. Many equipment parts bore United States Army Signal Corps markings and serial numbers. But the equipment inside is not only of advanced design, it's of meaningless design. The idea of printed circuits is fascinating, but understandable if not reproducible. Pentode amplifiers the size of a peanut are fascinating, not reproducible, and only vaguely understandable. For one thing, the filament isn't used at all; an indirectly heated cathode is a new item to them. However, the items that really stop them are several varieties of gadgets, all about the same size, but of violently different characteristics. There are units one eighth inch in diameter by about three fourths long which have resistance varying from one hundred to ten million ohms. Incredible, but true. Others have infinite resistance, and are condensers of capacity so high for their tiny size as to be unbelievable. Still others have three leads, and, opened, seem to be crystal detectors—understandable —but are amplifiers, which doesn't make sense. They also turn out to be nonreproducible. They are simple mechanical structures, using the very unusual element germanium, in the crystals. But the chemical expert's best purified germanium won't work when a reproduction is tried. (You've got to have the right amount of the right impurity introduced in the right way. Techniques in the '20s weren't up to it.)

Furthermore, there's a tube that's obviously a triode oscillator, but the frequency involved is so high as to be detectable only when using crystal detectors from the plane's own equipment. The circuit, too, doesn't make sense to the radio engineers, though the physicists from the Bureau of Standards finally figured it out. (It's a tuned-line oscillator operating at about four hundred megacycles. The physicists had to go back to Hertz's original work with tuned-rod oscillators to get a glimpse of what went on.) They can't reproduce the tube, and no tube they can make will oscillate in the circuit used.

Finally, there's another group of equipments they've simply agreed to forget. It seems to center around a permanent magnet of fantastic power which embraces a copper block drilled with holes of odd sizes, having a central electron-emitting rod through it. The magnetron is bad enough—obviously beyond reproduction, since the cathode can't be duplicated, the magnet can't be duplicated, and the metal-to-glass seals are beyond any available technique. But the associated equipment is worse. There is a collection of rectangular pipes made of heavy silver-plated copper. The pipes contain nothing, carry nothing, and appear totally meaningless. This time the physicists are completely stumped. (Wave-guide theory is a recent development; without some basic leads, and understanding of the order of frequencies involved, they'd never get there.) And worst of all, the physicists find that several bits of the equipment contain radioactive material. They know about radium, uranium, thorium, et cetera. But—this is highly radioactive, and it's *cobalt*. But cobalt isn't radioactive! But this is, and it is cobalt. (It's the transmit-receive tube; the radio-cobalt is used to keep it ready to ionize easily and instantly.) They also find radioactive emanations from much of the plane's material, with faint indications that half the elements in the chemical table are radioactive—which is arrant nonsense! (The guided missile had been flown through the fringes of an atomic bomb test gathering report data.)

In summary, the aerodynamicists report that the tailless monstrosity is interesting, but the principles of its design are confusing. The engine group report the "engine," so-called, can't be the engine. It was thought for a while that it might be a rocket, but since both ends are, and always were, wide open, it can't possibly be a rocket. The radio experts of the Signal Corps agree that some of the equipment is an immeasurably advanced type of radio apparatus, but the design is so advanced that it is futile to study it. It can't be reproduced, and involves principles evidently several centuries ahead of the knowledge of 1920—so advanced that the missing, intermediate steps are too many to be bridged. The mystery electronic equipment, called Equipment Group X, remains simply mysterious, save that, in some way, it involves a receiver operating on an unknown, but very high frequency. (By which they meant not the ten thousand megacycle input but the "low" frequency intermediate frequency amplifier, operating at only thirty megacycles. Having no means of generating thirty megacycles at that time, they could only say it was higher than the highest available. And they didn't, of course, recognize the ten kilomegacycle RF head as a receiver at all.)

The physicists would be inclined to ascribe it to Mars, Venus or any other non-terrestrial planet, if it weren't for the obvious Signal Corps markings. Since terrestrial cobalt isn't radioactive, and the cobalt in this ship is—

But anyway, the reports can only be tucked in the "File And Forget" division. About the only thing they can lift out of that piece of marvelous equipment is the secret of making good, small, high-resistance electronic resistors. The chemists and physicists did crack that one, and it's the answer to an electronicist's prayers; the tiny resistors are not wound with sub-microscopic resistance wire, as was at first believed—they're little ceramic tubes filled with a composition of clay and graphite which is such an extremely bad conductor that it does the job beautifully. By varying the composition, resistors of a standard size can range from one ohm to one hundred million.

At that, our 1920 group was really lucky. Suppose the item that fell through a time-fault had carried an atomic warhead. If it didn't go off, it would have presented the physicists with two of the most dangerous, utterly inexplicable lumps of matter imaginable. Pure U-235 or pure plutonium—that would have driven the chemists mad!—before they'd even discovered synthetic radioactivity. They would have been certain to kill themselves by bringing those two masses too close to each other, though, out of the bomb mechanism, they wouldn't have exploded.

But—write your own ticket, in your own special field. Let 1920, or 1910, or 1890 try to understand the functioning of any one of your modern gadgets. Even though, in those years, first-rate scientists with a full understanding of scientific methodology, and with fairly complete laboratory equipments, were available!

NOVEMBER   1948

"OUR CATALOGUE NUMBER . . ."

There's a great tendency on the part of a human being to say "It always seemed to me . . ." or "I never did believe that . . ." or the like. It's self-evidently true that the above statements cannot be true of any individual, in any instance whatsoever—not in the sense implied by the individual. Since no individual has existed forever, "always" is inherently inapplicable. Since no individual carried on active philosophical evaluational processes at birth, or immediately thereafter, "always" in the sense of "as long as I have existed" is never applicable.

But we're so ready to pretend that we haven't changed! The basic implication of such statements is simply "I am as I have been and as I will be . . . and furthermore, I'm right, have been, and will be."

As a long-time science-fictioneer, I run into that characteristic in its acute—and acutely irritating—phase. The fellow who "knows" that science fiction is nonsense—the one who, in 1941, "knew" rockets larger than Fourth of July fireworks were nonsense, but who, after reading that V-2s were landing one-ton lots of high explosive in London, instantaneously changed polarity, and "always knew" rockets could do that sort of thing. But who, as of 1944, "knew" atomic energy was nonsense—and as of August 8th, say, 1945, "always knew" we could do it.

The "interval of wonder" is astonishingly small in most people. Of course, eliminating it does make one feel smug, well satisfied with one's deep and cogent understanding of all things. But it seems to me you miss a lot of the fun of sensing the change around you! You know, no matter how fast you're going, you have no sense of motion; it's only the acceleration that you can detect. There's no kick to steady motion—the lift and thrill comes in detecting the great driving thrust that produces the change of speed.

A world of no change is boring beyond endurance—yet it seems to me that a lot of people are missing the immense and joyous stimulus of living in a period when the world is changing, accelerating, faster than it ever did before—by a sort of mental black-out. They blank out the acceleration period, like a rocket pilot who passes out during the 8g thrust of the take-off, regaining awareness only *after* the change of speed has been made.

We're only half aware of the immense thrust of civilization toward a higher speed of accomplishment. The change of level is something even the science-fictionally alerted individual can readily miss—because the acceleration is on so broad a scale. The non-science-fictioneer is apt to skip that interval of wonder completely—and it's not too easy for the science-fictioneer to find all of the intervals of wonder, the moments of mental acceleration when we recognize that a vague hope, a half-dream, has become a reality.

Dr. John Pomeroy, who's done a number of articles for the magazine, is an Argonne National Laboratory researcher—and far from sending me tidbits of classified information, has simply kept me aware of the standard catalogues and brochures of the industrial companies that offer various industrial components to interested markets. That supply of catalogues and standard commercial offerings I find far more exciting and intriguing. Talking about going to the Moon, or to Mars is interesting—but what counts is the day someone publishes their annual catalogue offering "'our catalogue number . . .' for the four-man scout, satisfactory for Lunar exploratory work, or asteroid prospectors; not recommended for gravitational fields exceeding fifty kilonewtons."

The booklets Dr. Pomeroy has sent along, during the last few years, are the "our catalogue number . . ." offerings that have reduced the science-fiction of 1940–45 to specific commercial models.

The Collins Radio Company offers, in their catalogue listings, radio receivers and transmitters intended for amateur and commercial installations—and also a cyclotron, standard commercial model, a packaged item ready for delivery and installation on order.

Just about twenty years ago, the cyclotron was the newest and furthest frontier of extremely advanced laboratory research.

General Electric, I understand, has an eighty megavolt betatron they are about ready to offer as a packaged unit for industrial application. Their smaller, twenty-five megavolt model is recommended for X-ray quality control inspection on heavy castings and forgings.

I got into theoretical physics back in 1928, because science fiction had convinced me that that was the field wherein the great advances would be made in my lifetime—atomic energy and the like. In 1932, the neutron was discovered, the cyclotron work began, and the real surge to crack the nucleus got under way.

The mass spectrograph was, at that time, a rare and wonderful device, possessed by a few of the most advanced university laboratories. Mass spectrographs are now offered on an "our catalogue number . . ." basis by a number of firms. Recording electro-spectrophotometers are offered for industrial labs, "in gray crackle or other finish. File space for storing recordings or other data built into the cabinet. A handsome piece of equipment in any laboratory."

Yes—the fact that it does automatically, and in a matter of seconds, something advanced university laboratories couldn't accomplish in weeks a few decades ago is not enough; by rights the technician properly holds that it should also be good looking, convenient, and make efficient use of space. Mass spectrographs, on the other hand, are advertised as useful devices for detecting leaks, and for production-line quality control inspection.

Robots are offered by several scores of companies; they aren't tin men, since no one wants a tin man for any valid industrial use, so they're called "automatic process control equipment" or the like—or "digital computer systems." But the computing machine that was, not more than a few years ago, a thing of rare wonder is now a standard catalogue item from dozens of companies. A recent issue of *Scientific American* carried a series of articles on cybernetics—but the advertisements that went with the articles were even more revealing. A popular, newsstand sale magazine carrying advertisements for standard trade devices that would be described only in science-fiction magazines as little as fifteen years ago!

The last batch of commercial catalogues I got from Dr. Pomeroy contains one that is still at least a little bit on the interval-of-wonder boundary. It's from Radiation Counter Laboratories, Inc., of Nucleonic Park, Skokie, Illinois—their "RCL Illustrated Price List No. 12." One of the first items offered, I see, is "A Handbook On Small Research Nuclear Reactors for Universities & Industry," $6.00 a copy (10% discount on 5 copies or more).

Then there's the "Oak Ridge Compensated Ionization Chamber, RCL Mark 17 Model 2," a neutron-sensitive instrument used in pile controls. Outside dimensions 3 feet long, by 3¾ inches diameter. $1,345.

They do not as yet, apparently, have a complete small nuclear reactor installation, with all control equipment and installation costs, offered as a packaged installation as a catalogue item. That may be a year or two more—but not much longer, I imagine.

I can't yet get quotations on that four-man scout ship—but I can, if I want, get quotations on eighty megavolt X-ray equipment, or small atomic power plants.

Of course, we always knew that would happen, didn't we?

JULY 1953

THE SCIENTIST

The philosophy of the true scientist is one of the few things he does not, ordinarily, express clearly; this is, in part, because he, of all men, considers human opinions of little import in the scheme of things, and a philosophy appears to be simply a system of human opinions. He's wrong in that to some degree; a philosophy is a theory of the relationships of the Universe, actually—and it is important to state theories clearly, communicate them, and cross-check them with the observations of others.

But because his personal philosophy is so personal, he seldom defines it clearly for others to investigate and consider. Perhaps it would be worth while seeking to find a definition—a clear statement—of the scientist's philosophy. Many of the fine scientists I know and have known appear to me to act on a system of beliefs somewhat like this:

They believe in the existence of a Supreme Authority in the Universe, an Authority they call "Natural Law." They hold that that Authority is above and beyond the opinions and beliefs, the will or willfulness, of any human being. That that Authority can, moreover, be directly consulted by any man, at any time— and that every man is, at every time and in every place, directly and specifically obedient to that Authority, to Natural Law, whether he recognizes that fact or not.

They believe that the highest task of Man is to seek to understand more fully the nature of the Laws of the Universe.

That the highest good of Man is achieved by understanding and working with those Laws, and not by seeking to defy them.

That the *system* of laws is absolutely inescapable, but that any *individual* law can be offset by proper use of others of the total system of laws. That Natural Law is like an equation having many terms; the total equation must always be in balance, but that any one factor on one side may be altered at will by accepting appropriate alteration of factors on the other side of the equation.

That Man thus has free choice with respect to any situation—but he cannot rationally speak of having free choice as to whether he will or will not obey the total system of the Laws of the Universe.

The scientist believes that *he* has made a mistake any time his actions lead to results he did not predict—and that it is sublimely futile to say that the Universe is wrong, or unjust, or irrational.

Since only total knowledge of everything in the total Universe could make possible accurate prediction of all the results of any action, the scientist is necessarily an humble man; he knows he must make mistakes.

But the scientist is also a proud man; he is proud of his willingness to learn, to give up his dearest conviction in the face of a new learning.

The scientist seeks to state his beliefs in the clearest, most unequivocal form he can achieve; thus he can more quickly detect and correct errors in his ideas as to what he thinks the Laws are, and what those Laws actually are.

The scientist seeks to communicate his ideas to other men of high ability and knowledge equal to his own; if he cannot communicate his idea to them, he knows he has not adequately clarified his statements, or has made some error in his development of his idea. He has made a mistake; it is futile to hold the other man at fault. This he learns early, for it is a simple extension of the concept of the futility of blaming the Universe when his experiment goes in a direction other than he predicted. Other people are, clearly, part of any individual scientist's external Universe.

The scientist likes to work with machines. A machine is a structure which has no beliefs, no biases, no willingness to be friendly nor any desire to be inimical, for it has *no* desires. It's utterly honest, granting no favors and refusing no earned reward. A man can fool himself; he can even fool his friends and, sometimes, his enemies. A machine is honest to a fault.

A machine invariably does precisely what you have "told" it to do; if your instructions—i.e., your design—are not clear, the machine does not function as predicted. If it doesn't, the fault is yours—you gave the instructions. Designing and building any type of machine is a powerful lesson in humility and, equally, in self-respect. If it works, you know precisely why it does; if it doesn't, you may not know why, but you must, inescapably, acknowledge an error, for the machine will not function until you do acknowledge that you have made an error, and both seek and find that error.

The true scientist is an humble man in another respect; he acknowledges that the Laws of the Universe apply in full to himself; that they limit him as well as others, and will equally help him as well as any other.

He is also a courageous man; he is willing to submit his tender and beloved beliefs to the harsh test of practice and experiment, well knowing that most of the time the experiment will prove him wrong and force him to rebuild, laboriously, the structure of belief he so recently completed.

To the nonscientist he seems very strange. The scientist looks at the Ptolmaic theory of the Universe, and the modern concept of the Cosmos, and says: "They are not very different; each yields the same predicted observations to the first decimal point." His understanding completely confuses the nonscientist, for the scientist holds that facts are very deceptive, yet also holds that all understanding must be based on fact. How can this be?

It's very confusing to the nonscientist to have an electrical engineer and a mechanical engineer get together and say that an automobile transmission gear shift is essentially the same thing as a multi-tapped transformer.

The resultant attitude the scientist shows toward his theories—the way he abandons one and shifts over to "an entirely different" one—makes him seem somehow intellectually dishonest, untrustworthy and unreliable to the nonscientist who cannot see the fundamental similarity of the theories. How can a man honestly say that an automobile gear shift is the same thing as a multi-tapped transformer? Only by recognizing that each is an impedance matching device, that each is a modification and application of the basic principle of the lever.

The scientist seeks the Basic Laws, and is not afraid to find that they apply to him—for he knows that they always *have* applied to him, and always will, whether he acknowledges them or not. The Law of Action and Reaction applied to Ug, the Caveman; it was Ug's ignorance of them that got him into trouble, for the Law applied whether he knew or not, whether he so willed or not. A Man-made law can seek to limit a human's freedom; the nonscientist many times confuses Man-made law and its effects with Man-discovered law and the results of that discovery. It was not Newton's discovery of the Law of Gravity that kept men from flying—it was the *existence* of the Law that did that. But it was Newton's discovery of the Law, plus the Wright's application of certain laws of aerodynamics, that finally led to Man's flight.

When Ug, the Caveman, caught a small boulder thrown at him, and staggered backward under the impact, he attributed the effect to the *stone*. This was a misattribution of effect; the effect was assigned to the wrong cause. The *stone*, which he could see and which had palpable existence, was obvious; the *momentum* never existed apart from the stone, and was not obvious—until Newton recognized it.

The scientist seeks to achieve a correct attribution of cause and effect; in doing so he invents nothing, generates no new laws, imposes no new limits on humanity. Knowing this, he is not averse to accepting that he is, was, and always will be ruled by the Laws of the Universe.

Characteristically, many human beings lack the willingness to accept that they obey laws they do not know exist. In the field of personality and human relations, for instance, there is a deep rebellion against the idea that there are laws which apply. In that area, then, there are very few true scientists in the sense of individuals willing to acknowledge freely that they are bound by and controlled by Universal Laws they do not know exist.

But one of the most difficult tasks any physical scientist can try is that of defining in what way his basic philosophy differs from that of the sincere, self-searching moral philosopher, with his deep belief in God as the Supreme Authority, and the Giver of Universal Law. Perhaps it is, essentially, that the physical scientist says, in effect, "I have proven beyond doubt that there is Universal Law; I am not yet wise enough to know the nature of its source," while the moral philosopher insists that he knows the Source.

It might help the integration of the physical, social and moral philosophical sciences, however, if each group could state in clearly communicable terms the essence of their beliefs. And this in turn would, surely, help in the integration of our vastly increasing physical competence with our laggard social engineering competence.

DECEMBER 1953

RELATIVELY ABSOLUTE

Human beings are so highly complex that, to date, no one of them has ever succeeded in figuring out (a) what he is, (b) what he wants, (c) where he's been, or (d) where he's going. Inasmuch as this includes you, me, and the rest of our friends, neighbors, and Wise Men, we need neither laugh nor shake our heads—though the gyrations resulting from the confusion above stated certainly range from the hilarious to the appalling.

Currently, the Russians are claiming that most of the major inventions of the last couple of centuries were originally made by inhabitants of that area of the world now known as the U.S.S.R. The suggestion that these inventors, who accomplished so much, lived and prospered under a Czarist society would not be welcome, in all probability. The fact that the inventors of the claimed devices generally recognized in the rest of the world—Bell, for example, as inventor of the telephone—lived in the capitalist countries is unacceptable to the Soviets, apparently. The Russian capitalist-era inventors are more acceptable, however, than non-Russian capitalist-area inventors.

This is, perhaps, an original reaction, unique to Russian Communists?

The history books available in this country's schools have a certain touch of precisely the same mechanism. Invention made by the now-enemy must be denied; invention made by the no-longer-dangerous enemy can be accepted safely.

The history books give Greece and Rome credit for starting modern science—which happens to be an extremely serious error. It's serious because it obscures an uniquely important fact: That only two cultures in the recorded history of Man have developed that combination of philosophical analysis and experimental cross-checking known as Modern Science. Greece and Rome are not among those two; neither culture achieved anything that hadn't been achieved elsewhere, and achieved a lot earlier. Oh, certainly there were details that only Rome, or only Greece achieved; it's also true that only the Greeks invented Greek as a language. The important thing is that other peoples had languages also.

The Chinese and Egyptians achieved high-order engineering several millennia before Rome did. Egypt's earliest engineering works were older, when Julius Caesar built his bridge across the Rhine, than Rome's monuments are today.

The Greeks did a lot with mathematics and geometry. The Babylonians had done so long before; the Egyptian surveyors of a few millennia before Rome was founded did considerable first-rate math, too. The Chinese had Pythagoras' Theorem worked out, too.

The Incas, quite independently, achieved a military road system that put Rome's to shame. The Mayas had a calendar far superior to that the Greeks and Romans developed.

Observation was old. Mathematics was old. It had been done before, and in many, many places, by many, many peoples. Rome's engineering feats weren't unique.

What we know as Western Culture is a highly hybridized product of much intermingling—and has the consequent hybrid vigor. Now the curious thing about it is that there's a great tendency to resist being hybridized, and consequently a great tendency to deny that hybridization has taken place. The Western Culture is, essentially, a hybrid resultant of Judeo-Christian philosophy, based on the old Semitic fundamentals, plus Greco-Roman admixtures, plus one other highly important admixture. The Greco-Roman-Semitic philosophy hybrid resultant had not done too well by the year 1000 A.D. The Dark Ages were not to be confused with Periclean Athens as an era of intellectual achievement. They say human beings want security; they had achieved it in Europe during that period. It was a magnificently static situation; nobody learned anything new, and nobody got upset by having to face a new idea for several centuries.

"Modern History" usually is measured from the beginning of the active phase of the Renaissance. What started the Renaissance?

Our unwashed, louse-ridden, feudal, and essentially barbaric ancestors had had their thick heads knocked together vigorously, and been unceremoniously pitched out on their ears by the highly civilized, powerfully progressive Islamic peoples. That happened not once, but four successive times. With the typical barbarian's assurance that they know all there is to know that's important, the Europeans had tried marching into Palestine.

They were trounced with appalling thoroughness and ease. They never established more than a minor beachhead against an Empire that stretched from Spain to India. Their nuisance value was minor, and if they could just be induced to behave in a semi-civilized manner, they were welcome to make any pilgrimages they desired.

During World War II, when the Russians drove through into Germany and the other Western European areas, their troops for the first time came into intimate contact with how the Western peoples live—what the actual Western standard of living is. It certainly isn't perfect, and is a long sight lower than it should be —but it infected the Russian troops with new and, for them, fabulously high ideas of how to live.

I suspect the same sort of thing happened to the Crusaders from Europe. Islam was civilized; Europe was not. Islam had achieved what no other civilization Man had developed had been able to; it invented Science.

Rome didn't, and Greece didn't; they had each produced one of the two ingredients—as had many another people before them, and other peoples also produced independently after them. Philosophy is fine—but it won't stand alone. Athens fell flat on its beautifully philosophical face—for lack of an even passable sewage and water system. Rome had magnificent sanitary engineering systems—and fell flat on the problem of philosophy.

Neither people ever cross-checked philosophy *and* engineering. The Romans had no respect for the airy-fairy philosophy of the Greeks; the Greeks never respected the harsh, materialistic Romans.

We did *not* get our legacy of Science from Rome or Greece; we got it from Islam, the only people who invented it in all human history!

We should laugh at Russia's curious maneuvers with inventors? We, who, because Islam was, at the time, the great and dangerous enemy, preferred to attribute their inventions to the long-conquered enemy, Rome and Greece? The early Christians hated Rome with a holy and burning hatred; read the New Testament's all out vilification of Rome! But that battle against Roman culture was long since won; it was safe, in 1400 A.D., to say that Romans and Greeks had been great and wise.

Islam was the enemy! *They* couldn't be wise or great!

So even a Czarist achievement is better than an American or French achievement in the eyes of the U.S.S.R.

Yes, I think we've played that same old game before. It has a familiar ring, even though the names are different. Some things that happen for the first time—aren't. Propaganda is much older than the word "propaganda." George Orwell's "Ministry of Truth" is much older than "1984."

The business about Islam, moreover, is important to the development of Mankind—because while Rome and Greece did not develop anything basically new, Islam did. And if we hide the fact that Islam, not Rome or Greece, invented science, we will miss the area in which must lie a unique force. Rome and Greece did *not* have that unique force; as pointed out above, many other peoples developed logic, mathematics and engineering. Studying Rome and Greece for the source-force that generated that unique thing, Science, therefore, would lead to frustration. You won't be able to find it, no matter how finely you comb the records; it wasn't there in the first place.

The contribution of Islam has been heavily occluded by propaganda started in the age when the West and Islam were struggling. Actually, most of our basic sciences are heavily larded with Arabic terminology. Chemistry has dropped the old Arabic prefix *al-* from its own name, but retains it in *alcohol*—the Mohammedans invented distillation—and a number of other instances. The *alembic* is no longer used, but chemists need the Arabic numerals—borrowed from India—and *al*gebra.

One of the major troubles was the chemists didn't borrow enough. Lavoisier is credited with introducing the balance into chemical investigations. But as early as the eighth century (A.D.) the Arab chemist Yber-Abou-Moussah-Djafer Al-Sofi reported that when metallic lead is heated and calcined in air, the resulting compound is heavier than the original metal. Somebody must have been using the balance a bit before Lavoisier thought of it.

Now at the time of Islam's greatest achievement, their influence extended from Spain to India. They were in contact with Hindu, Chinese and other civilizations. But, curiously, only two cultures in the history of Mankind have either invented or accepted Science. The highly civilized Chinese neither invented it, nor accepted it from the Arabs. The Hindus, likewise, failed either to invent or accept it. The Christians didn't invent it—but they did accept it.

In this, I mean by "science" that method of learning that involves the equal interaction and cross-checking of philosophical-theoretical thought, and actual physical-reality experiments, done as a conscious process for the consciously stated purpose of increasing knowledge and understanding—that is, increasing data and relationship-of-data.

Why? Why only these two?

Unquestionably, in any system so complex as a human culture, there is more than one factor. But we can find a factor that is present in these two, and missing in the others that achieved greatly—but didn't achieve Science.

The Scientific cultures have an Absolutistic philosophy—and a monotheistic philosophy. Remember that "religion" is, by derivation, the study of "the laws of things"—or "cosmology" in modern linguistic terms.

Both Mohammedanism and Christianity stem from the old Jewish philosophy of One God—an Absolute God, whose laws were absolute, and could be appealed only to the One Absolute God.

The Greeks were in a quite different Universe. It didn't have any single set of laws or rules; if Zeus made a ruling, one you found irksome, you could try getting Athena or Poseidon or Aphrodite, maybe, to change it. If there was some curious phenomenon observed—observe it and forget it. The whim of a god isn't lasting; some other god will change it. The smart man will study texts on "The Psychology and the Rivalries of the Gods," because that's the only way to get anywhere.

If an ancient Greek observed that it took longer to boil an egg on top of a mountain than it did at sea level—so what? You fool, don't you know Zeus and Poseidon dislike each other? Poseidon rules water; Zeus rules the upper air. What do you think is going to happen to water when you take it up nearer the upper air? Naturally it doesn't work as well.

And if you study Platonic philosophy, and find that it has certain uncomfortably binding restrictions on your actions—why the Sophist school is just as logical. It just appeals to other Gods—er, I mean other *postulates*—but it's just as logical, isn't it? Of course. And there's no need to stay with it, if it proves irksome; there are other philosophies, too.

A polytheistic cosmology is not going to lead to the development of science. Science is, moreover, going to be a mighty unpopular philosophy in any culture; it has an absolutism about it that says "It makes no difference who you are, what you are, or what you want. Neither does it matter what your wealth is, or your political power. These are The Laws; obey or suffer."

It could be considered, even, only by a culture that had already accepted the idea of an Absolute Power in the Universe.

The great difficulty with that problem is that, once you've found that Absolutes do exist—you're apt to go sort of absolutistic about it, and say "These are the Absolute Laws—and these are *absolutely all* the laws."

The Jewish people invented the monotheistic philosophy that made science possible—but they didn't invent science. They had too much of the absolute, perhaps. The Arabs were relatively absolute—and invented Science.

Christians and Jews have done fine with it ever since; until very recently *nobody else has been able to!*

It rather looks, then, as though Einstein's relativity is an essential part of the philosophy necessary to developing Science—but must be recognized as being necessary, but not sufficient. There is reason to believe that *both* relatives *and* absolutes are necessary to a developing science—that either, if held to be the

Be All and End All of the matter leads to stagnation and non-achievement.

Now it is interesting that the whole progress of science has centered around that area where there are Absolutes—the areas where no man has a right to his own opinion. The progress made in the social sciences, where opinion has been dominant, and everything has been fanatically relative, has been very small indeed. Psychology claims to be a "young science"; we can go into that question some other time, but it's worth pointing out that Aristotle did a fine textbook on psychology, sociology and anthropology some two-thousand-odd years ago. "The Confessions of St. Augustine" has a most thoughtful and intelligent study of guilt feelings. The Aesculapian priests of Greece were using narcosynthesis—drug hypnotherapy—some twenty-five hundred years ago. The age of the Hindu *Vedda* is considerably disputed, but it's not much younger—and has considerable data on clinical psychosomatic medicine using hypnotherapy. There's really been astonishingly little progress in the humanic sciences in the last few millennia.

The progress has all been in those areas where dear old Mother Nature took a club to Man's thick skull, and said, in effect, "This is the unit you'll use—whether you like it or not. Your opinion on the matter is completely unimportant. And yes, Tom, your opinion *is* just as good as Dick's or Harry's—and all three are no good whatever." Where Nature supplied absolutely non-relative *units*, like atoms and photons, Science got somewhere.

Want to have some fun with the relativity formulas? Try taking some different units, and see what happens to them! The relativity formulas involve a lot of higher power terms—squares, cubes, and higher. If you take your unit of velocity *not* as centimeters per second, but as c, then all the higherpower terms of c reduce to 1.00, no matter what the power is. Then the v terms all become fractional, and higher powers of fractions are *smaller* values than the original fraction, whereas higher powers of quantities greater than 1.000 are increased by self-multiplication. By picking the right set of self-consistent units, you can make the most marvelous hash out of the relativity formulas—without altering the formulas an iota!

And if we've got a relativistic universe, with no absolutes in it, then I can play deuces-wild with the units. You start being relativistic, and I'll relativistic you right out of business! I'll make as much of a mess out of your science as the humanic scientists have made out of theirs. All I need is the right to make my choice of units purely a matter of personal preference!

JULY 1954

Words are simply sound-symbols for concepts; the meaning of a sound-symbol is not rigidly, unchangeably connected to a concept, so subtle change can readily set in. And usually does, of course, unless specific efforts are made to establish a solid, rigid correlation between symbol and concept. Science has made progress largely by reason of working with hard, rigid definitions, and sticking to them. That's the only way you can discover you're stuck with one—and admit the need for a change of concept.

But outside of science, the concepts sort of ooze out from under a symbol, without anyone actually admitting the change has taken place. The only way you can check, then, is to recall the old, pragmatic dictum, "I don't care what you say; what do you *do?*" Physical science has accepted rigid definitions, because physical science is one hundred per cent concerned with action-doing. An electron is a concept—but the term refers to a pattern of behavior, of *doings*.

I want to discuss a certain American sound-symbol, one that has badly slipped its moorings. Discussing the symbol is pretty useless, under such circumstances, because it can be shown that "history proves that . . ." by referring to what that sound-symbol *did* refer to. So let's set up a brand-new, nonsense word and define it in terms of action-doing. Reason: We'll have a term which, *as a term,* has no historical values whatever. We'll be forced to discuss the historical value of the action-doing system it refers to, because the term itself has no history.

Then we can, later, cross-check with the historical terms, and see how much, and in what direction, the terms have slipped.

Let's use the term "gwolic system" to refer to a particular economic philosophy. We'll define a "gwolic system" as a system under which major units of economic production are allowed to be controlled in an essentially arbitrary manner by individuals who gain their position by demonstrating unusual competence and ability. The individual executive under this system is not responsible to any higher authority for his individual decisions, but is held accountable for the over-all success or failure of his stewardship.

Under the gwolic system, the individual who shows executive competence by maintained over-all success, is automatically able to achieve the same type of arbitrary, individually-determined control over greater and greater economic units.

Mistakes he may make, causing a loss, he need not explain nor account for to anyone else, so long as his net average performance is as good or better than that of his highest-ranking competitor.

However, under the gwolic system, if his average is surpassed by a competing executive . . . he's out.

The system is, obviously, a little rugged on the individual executive; there is no guarantee of job-security, nor any reward for length of service.

But it has marked advantages from the viewpoint of the economy as a whole. It assures that the major productive units of the economy will be in the hands of individuals of exceptionally high competence. And the control is not determined on a basis of predetermined theory or ideology, but on the harsh, pragmatic test of workability.

Further, workability is necessary, but not sufficient. If John Jones has made the economic unit under his control work, and work well . . . that's only enough to hold the job temporarily. As soon as someone comes along who can make it *more* workable, John Jones is out, and the new man is in.

Notice that the executive is free to make any arbitrary decision that he, personally, thinks is sound—and no over-riding board peering over his shoulder reviews those decisions before they're acted on. He's a dictator, free to impose his opinions on the economic unit under his control. The only limitation imposed on him is that the net result of his actions must be advantageous.

That this system would lead to high productivity, and a maximum rate of growth is fairly evident. That it would be hard on the individual executive is also obvious. It would also, of course, be hard on the individuals employed in the economic unit when the executive did make a major blunder.

So much for a definition-description of a "gwolic system."

Now what historical name does this system correspond to?

The old-fashioned Capitalistic system, of course. The executive accumulated control over a major economic unit by accumulating capital; he owned the resultant unit, and managed it on a private-decision basis, without supervisory control. If he managed it well, on the average, his executive power was increased by further accumulation. If he slipped once or twice, he learned from the experience . . . or, if he didn't learn, he went bankrupt, and the control passed to others who could do better.

Further, if he was doing a good job, but another man came along who could do better . . . control was gradually taken from him, and the wiser executive gained.

The individual executive, under that system, was uncontrolled in so far as immediate decisions were concerned . . . but definitely controlled by loss of economic control if he continued to fall behind.

Now let's consider another type of system, one we'll call a "ngoric system." A ngoric system is characterized by committee-and-theory control of economic units. Executives are appointed, but they operate under policy established by the committee, acting on an agreed-on theory of How It Should Be. The immediate success or failure of the economic unit so controlled is not so important; the realization of the theoretical goal established is. Thus, even if one economic unit continues to function at a loss for a considerable period, it will be maintained, because the theory requires that it be done that way. Even an economic unit that does not work can be maintained under the ngoric system, because it *should* be.

The larger the scope of the committee and theory, the less workability of any one economic unit matters, and the less important competence of the executive becomes.

The ngoric system has obvious advantages; for handling long-range projects involving a long period of initiation, it is self-evidently excellent. The mammals, in essence, introduced the ngoric system, when they introduced long-term care of the young. The young are always incompetent, and an economic loss, until a very large investment of time, effort, and energy has developed them.

It's also the ngoric system that makes research laboratories possible. Governments, too, operate largely on the ngoric system.

What historical term corresponds to this defined system? The Socialistic system, of course; it is a system wherein government committees, operating under theory, appoint executives to operate economic units. The fact that an economic unit isn't producing adequately doesn't mean that anything is wrong in a socialistic system; the theory is important, not the practice. If it's a thing that *should* work, then patience, and continued subsidy, is sure to make it succeed.

Of course, it's a little hard to tell whether the personnel of the project is competent; the mere fact that their project isn't getting anywhere doesn't prove anything, of course. It takes time for these things. And it *is* difficult to get satisfactory executives for Socialistic programs; so many of the highly competent individuals are so impatient with theories, and show such poor acceptance of proper organizational procedure and discipline. They keep tending to act on their own, instead of consulting the committee before making any moves.

And now the big question: Which type of system—Capitalistic or Socialistic—does the United States have today?

Socialistic, of course. Yes, I know they *say* it's Capitalistic . . . but what do they *do?* Can a major economic unit make a move today without consulting with some series of committees? If it isn't the Securities Exchange Commission, it's the Federal Trade Commission, the Federal Communications Commission, a state Utilities Commission, or, at minimum, some Labor Committee. Congress doesn't have the power to make executive decisions for private capital companies like the American Telephone and Telegraph Company, of course. But the Department of Justice forced their subsidiary, the Bell Telephone Laboratories, to renounce its rights under the Patent Law. (As it did also for IBM, and is in process of doing to RCA.) And, of course, the Federal Communications Commission rulings determine what the company executives must do. And it was long ago pointed out that "the power to tax is the power to destroy," which fact both Congress and the A.T.&T. thoroughly appreciates.

No executive of a major economic unit in this country is free to operate without half a dozen committees peering over his shoulder. No economic moves involving finance can be undertaken without *first* consulting the Securities Exchange Commission.

Meanwhile, the railroads operate almost uniformly in a state of quasi-bankruptcy. They, the only inherently efficient long-haul, heavy-duty transportation system, are being taxed and unionized into inoperable condition.

Now, on the other hand, let's see what kind of economic system the vaunted Union of Soviet Socialist Republics has.

Practically pure gwolic! Sure, the executive may be called a "commissar" instead of "owner"—but he's an executive having direct, personal authority over major economic units, held responsible for the over-all success of his unit, but not for his individual decisions toward that end.

Ah, me, how the symbols and the referent concepts do ooze around!

Soviet Russia has, in all the action-doing particulars, an almost pure Capitalistic system . . . while the Capitalistic United States has an almost pure Socialistic economy!

One thing remains true; the gwolic system, under whatever other name you put it, has historically proven, again and again, the system that gets the most real accomplishment in the least time. It worked wonderfully for the Americans, when we had it, and it seems to be doing great things for the Russians now.

It always was a good system. Too bad we gave it up.

AUGUST 1957

RESEARCH IS ANTISOCIAL

Xrays weren't discovered by logical deduction, followed by a logically constructed, crucial experiment; they were called "Xrays"
because, when Roentgen first observed the effect, it was a complete, and unexplainable surprise. Unexplainable—and therefore,
of course, unpremeditatable, unpredictable, and unplanned.

It was not the result of sound, scientifically organized research.
It just happened.

What do we mean by the term "research" today?

I believe it can be shown that there are two broad classes of
search-into-the-unknown, two classes that can be sharply differentiated in the sense "north" and "south" can be clearly and
sharply differentiated. They are opposite *directions*—though it's
perfectly obvious that New York City is north of Washington although it's south of Montreal. If you want to confuse an issue,
obfuscate a point, if you want simply to defeat an argument, that
makes things easy. Just confuse direction with position, and you
can argue both ends against the middle, pick either side you want
and "prove" it. "You can't say that New York is north! Why, it's
certainly not even in the arctic zone!"

The two directions of search-of-the-unknown we might call *exsearch* and *insearch;* together, they constitute *research.*

By "insearch," I mean that class of search-of-the-not-yet-known
which involves deducing the meaning implicit in the set of postulates we are working with—"making the self-evident obvious."
Ideally, a sufficiently well designed, and sufficiently large logical
machine, such as the direct lineal descendants of the modern
electronic computers might be, could carry insearch to comple-
tion, and deduce *all* the consequences of a given set of postulates.

Theoretically, at least, a logic machine could deduce from Euclid's postulates, all the theorems of Euclidean geometry. Since
this involves exhausting an infinity, the thing can't be done by

any existable machine; see Isaac Asimov's "Hemoglobin and the Universe" for a detailed development of why it can't.

Insearch, then, is an infinite field; unlimited work can be done in deducing the consequences of a given set of postulates.

But . . . notice very carefully that "infinity" *is not "all"!* Although a logic machine could theoretically deduce *all* the consequences of Euclidean geometry, this term "all" is not the same as the term "all" in the phrase "all possible geometrical theorems."

There's the old pseudo-syllogism about the cat-o'-nine-tails:

1. Any cat has one more tail than no cat.
2. No cat has eight tails.
3. Therefore, any cat has nine tails.

The trick, of course, is that "no cat" means two totally different things in the first two statements.

"All consequences of Euclid's postulates" is a limited infinity— it's infinite, but bounded. It's like an asymptotic curve; it goes on forever, yet it never gets beyond certain limits.

And the theorems of curved spaces lie outside the limits of Euclidean geometry. Therefore the logical machine, even if it exhausted the infinity of Euclidean geometry, would none the less never reach curved-space theorems.

The logic machine type of search is *insearch*—an infinite, but bounded field.

By *exsearch*, I mean search for the unknowns *outside the limits of known postulates.*

Einstein's work, of course, was exsearch; he went outside the limits of Euclidean geometry, which, up to that time, had been considered *the* laws of real-world space. Einstein didn't originate the curved-space geometry; the postulate Einstein transcended was the one which held "Euclidean geometry describes real-world space." Only by going outside the bounds of that postulate —doing exsearch outward from the known limits—was it possible to achieve Relativity.

No possible deductions staying within the then-known limits— no logic machine, however immense or rapid—could have gone from Newtonian physics and Euclidean geometry to Relativity. It couldn't have, because the postulate "Euclidean geometry applies to real-world space," would have forced it to cancel out as inconsistent any deductions that led in that direction.

Exsearch is, necessarily, contralogical; it transcends the logical bounds. However, the moment it has done so, and established a new outpost in the thitherto Unknown Outside . . . that immediately becomes a new postulate, so the area is instantly inside the new postulate system!

Research necessarily includes both processes—and if either one is omitted, the result is not true research.

Under current social dogma, *research is antisocial!* Only insearch is socially acceptable; if you cut a process in two, and throw away one half, you do *not* have the process any more.

To show that a particular culture holds a particular postulate concept is always difficult. To show that our own culture holds a postulate concept which it denies holding is extremely difficult . . . when you're trying to show that to members of that culture!

Certainly America vigorously insists on its high regard and belief in the value of Research.

Yes . . . but . . . "I know what you *say*, but what do you *do?*"

What America does in fact value most highly is insearch. But exsearch is culturally rejected, and exsearchers are punished!

Let me validate that statement.

The most highly organized group of professional scientists, with the longest period of recognition as a group, and the group most fully expressed in legislation, is that of the Medical Doctors. The forces that are still vague and poorly focused in other fields have had time to crystallize and clarify their consequences in Medicine. It takes time to work out the logically deducible consequences of any given set of postulates, in the older field of Medicine, those postulates have been worked out. Therefore the results are more clearly visible.

The same essential forces are at work elsewhere; I start with Medicine solely because it has had more time to clarify the consequences of those forces.

A culture expresses its philosophy in its laws; if the philosophy holds human life cheap, so do the laws. If the philosophy accepts slavery, there are laws about slavery. If the cultural philosophy accepts research, there are laws about research. Patent laws, for example. The laws regulating Medicine represent the interaction of the philosophy of Medicine itself, and the culture; each finds expression in the resultant legislation. If either Medicine or the culture were violently, fundamentally opposed to an idea, the laws would be changed. The present situation is decades old.

It is, then, legitimate to argue that whatever the laws hold represents something not unacceptable to the philosophy both of Medical Science and American culture.

Suppose a patient comes to a doctor, and careful examination reveals that he has leukemia. His own doctor sends him to specialists, to a clinic, and it is definitely determined that this individual has leukemia.

As of now, leukemia is an invariably fatal disease; the treatment methods accepted as standard by Medical Science, in other words, invariably fail to produce cure. The mortality rate is one hundred per cent.

Now consider two possibilities:

1. The doctor treats his patient according to standard Medical procedures.

2. The doctor treats his patient according to an unorthodox technique of his own.

If he uses Standard Operating Procedure, he knows with very high certainty that his patient will die. He does so; the patient dies.

If he uses an unorthodox treatment of his own on a group of patients, let us say he gets a thirty per cent rate of cure, while seventy per cent of his patients die.

Under the second situation, the doctor can be harassed by malpractice suits by the family of any of his patients who die. If he used the orthodox procedure, *in the full knowledge that it would fail,* he cannot be prosecuted.

The culture, and Medical Science are in full agreement; if it is orthodox, it's "good," even if it never works—but if it is unorthodox, it is "bad," even if it succeeds!

Suppose a doctor treats a leukemia patient by a new and unorthodox method, and the patient survives, recovers completely, but his unorthodox curative drug causes a side-effect that produces complete loss of hair. The doctor can be sued by the patient.

When Ehrlich introduced 606 as a treatment for syphilis, some individuals died of arsenic poisoning as a result of its use. Ehrlich was violently attacked; it took a trial to clear him.

If a doctor used an unorthodox method, and used it successfully—he would still be liable to expulsion from the Medical Society.

Now *if* the doctor could show that his unorthodox treatment both worked, and was logically deducible from accepted postulates—he would be let off with a very severe warning, and most definitely told not to do *that* again.

Reason: He violated the postulate: "All new treatments must be accepted by the Authorities before they can be tried."

Both Medical Science and the culture must approve in actual fact of this attitude expressed in our laws: if it's orthodox, it's good, even if it never works, while the unorthodox must never be tried, even if the orthodox method is known to fail every time.

Now consider passing a law to this effect: That a doctor who uses a known method of treatment, under circumstances wherein it is known to fail invariably, is guilty of malpractice and may be sued by his patients.

An immediate consequence of this would be that every doctor who used standard, orthodox treatment on leukemia patients would automatically be open to a malpractice suit. Those methods are *known* to be inadequate; why, then, should the society tolerate their continued use?

Under such a situation, doctors would be forced to do exsearch work on the problem. Inevitably, some progress would be made. The time, effort, and money now being thrown away on known-to-be-useless treatment of leukemia victims would, at least, yield some genuine research benefits to the society.

Treatment by rubbing with redistilled essence of rattlesnake oil could not be less valuable than treatment by a method *known* to be futile.

But—to establish such a situation is to establish the proposition that exsearch is a tolerable, even a valuable thing.

Obviously, no matter what the culture, and Science may *say* about that, the simple fact that the laws are what they are show that they *do* something entirely different. They *do* suppress exsearch vigorously.

As I said, I cite Medical Science only because it is longest established, and most thoroughly embodied in laws. The fact that the culture accepts those laws shows clearly that the philosophy behind them must be not-unacceptable to the culture. Then we should be able to find the same philosophy expressed elsewhere in the culture, though perhaps not codified in so clear a form as in the medico-legal instance.

Consider a business executive's problem when an inventor comes to him and claims he has a wonderful new idea.

The executive's first move is to call in his professional experts in the field involved.

Assume that there is no professional jealousy whatever involved; that the professional experts are honest, sincere, and well-trained, and that the inventor's idea involves an exsearch step that flatly violates what they *know* to be true.

The professional experts turn down the idea. "It's manifestly impossible; it would involve a violation of Frahmstahl's Law if it did work! If he presents a 'demonstration' of his idea, it must necessarily be a hoax . . . or at best it's a mistake."

If the executive plays a hunch, and backs the inventor, despite the honest advice of the professional experts . . . his board of directors will be decidedly hard to satisfy. His action is not logically defensible. Even if the inventor has presented a demonstration that convinces the executive, his action is still indefensible in view of the testimony of the experts.

Furthermore, even if the inventor proves to be right, and his device does actually work, the executive will *still* have a rough time with his Board! Even under these conditions, their attitude will be, "Welllll . . . you got away with it this time, but only by luck! Don't ever do any such illogical thing again, though; understand?!"

In a logic-based culture, only logically defensible research is acceptable—and that means insearch only.

We hear a lot of discussion of the vital necessity of more "fundamental research" today.

Take a look at the laws—at what our culture *does*—and judge what "research" means to them.

Somebody formulated the motto: "Don't undertake vast projects with half-vast people."

A research plan that tolerates only insearch, and punishes exsearch, however big a project it may be, is only a half-vast program.

APRIL 1958

PHYSICIAN, HEAL THYSELF

THE VALUE OF PANIC

There's a well-known and well-hated law of laboratory experiment that goes, "In a laboratory experiment, if something can go wrong . . . it will."

"Wrong" in this sense usually means that a random factor gets in, where none is supposed to be. And random factors, by definition, can do anything. It could even improve the results of the experiment, of course.

Dr. Wayne Batteau, of the Harvard School of Applied Science, has been studying the basic structure of the scientific method from the viewpoint of Information Theory analysis. One of the interesting logical results—translated from symbols into English—is "In total ignorance, try anything. Then you won't be so ignorant."

Let's add a third item; all higher animal life-forms display the characteristic that, when under extreme environmental pressure, they can go into panic behavior, acting with great violence and determination in a manner entirely different from the normal behavior patterns of the organism. This applies all the way up to and including man.

Usually, panic behavior is characterized by its ineffectiveness or complete inappropriateness. The woman who tosses the mirror out the window of her burning home, and carries the pillow carefully down the stairs, is essentially similar in behavior to the chicken that, panicked by the rapidly approaching automobile, runs frantically, squawking, for home . . . into the path of the car.

Panic certainly appears to be an utterly negative, useless, and destructive characteristic, and has almost invariably been so labeled.

Maybe it isn't, though. If it were so completely useless, why would three billion years of evolution have yielded organisms which, quite uniformly, retain the characteristic?

Perhaps Dr. Batteau's statement of the case is applicable. Given: An organism with N characteristic behavior modes available. Given: An environmental situation which cannot be solved by any of the N available behavior modes, but which must be solved immediately if the organism is to survive. Logical conclusion: The organism will inevitably die. But . . . if we introduce Panic, allowing the organism to generate a purely random behavior mode *not* a member of the N modes characteristically available?

When the probability of survival is zero on the basis of all known factors—it's time to throw in an unknown. Panic is not logical—but it is most exceedingly sensible, as a basic mechanism of evolution!

If an organism is being attacked by a predator, the predator has a plan of campaign all figured out. It knows the characteristic behavior of its prey, what its defensive and evasive maneuvers are, and how to compensate those variables. For the predator, it's a sort of laboratory experiment.

But the experiment can go wrong, if the victim can introduce a purely random, uncompensated, and unpredicted factor. It *might* cause his survival.

Panic behavior is, necessarily, unlikely to yield useful results—the probability of any particular random act leading to success is pretty small. But—an organism doesn't use panic in a random fashion; it uses the panic mechanism only after all known, high-probability methods have been ruled out as having no probability of success. Under those conditions, panic has the maximum probability of success, simply because it never has a zero probability!

If I ask the question, "What number am I thinking of?" you have a certain, extremely small chance of guessing the right answer. But if you answer "Isaac Newton," the probability of that being correct is, obviously, zero. When a certain pattern is specifically, and positively known to be a wrong answer, then any random pattern has a higher probability.

These simple facts have a very great bearing on an important human problem; the problem of the quack doctor, particularly the cancer quack. The method of attack on the problem now being used specifically has zero probability of success; it is inherently futile to pass laws against him, because three billion years of evolution have established that his function is necessary!

Consider this: John Brown, rich bachelor, without family, is found to have cancer. It happens to be a type which cannot be treated by surgery, radiation, or drugs; it is inoperable, incurable, and inevitably lethal. The best and most competent medical experts examine him, and assure him that there is nothing that medical science can do.

If John Brown is a sane, rational man, and believes that his doctors are competent and expert, he will recognize that it is now time to go into panic. He will reject any further medical consultations, because he has been assured, by the best available authorities, that medical technique has zero probability of helping. The only rational thing to do, if he trusts the competence of his doctors, is to look for non-medical help. *Any other course of action is irrational.*

It will be far more rational for John Brown to go to a hex doctor in the Pennsylvania hills, or to a South American Indian witch doctor, than to a licensed M.D., he has been authoritatively informed by doctors who know medical technology thoroughly, that medical technology cannot help. No one knows enough about the technology of a hex doctor to make such an authoritative statement; therefore it is perfectly rational to try *anything other than a licensed* M.D. A licensed M.D. is the one type of healer he *knows* cannot help him.

He may try mysticism, astrology, herbal remedies, psychotherapy, or any unlicensed, unorthodox, medically-rejected quack. The very fact that the quack has been rejected by medical science is John Brown's assurance that he has some idea that medical science does not have.

He will be perfectly sensible and rational to spend every nickel of his fortune in this way, so long as he does *not* spend it with regularly licensed physicians!

Only if John Brown does *not* trust his original doctors to have full and competent knowledge of medical technology can he have reason to visit another orthodox M.D.

John Brown is in an environmental situation of lethal stress, and overwhelming immediacy; he might donate his money to the American Cancer Society—but there'll be another John Brown's body mouldering in the grave, which is what concerns him.

Trying to legislate against the quack cancer doctor is trying to prevent the ancient human right to try anything, when all known methods fail. There isn't anything more ultimately hopeless than to seek to prevent a man who knows he has no chance within the orthodox framework from trying unorthodox methods. Furthermore, it's inherently unethical; if medical science cannot help the man—they have no business whatever trying to deny him help from any other source, whether they think that other source is valid or not.

The Panic Experiment is an inherent right of every living entity; three billion years of evolution shows it makes sense. The one thing that a wise therapy organization can do is to help the Panic Experimenters, and allow them to help humanity by making their Panic Experiments—their random, try-anything experiments—as efficiently useful in gathering understanding as possible.

It's an ancient, basic right, that right to try anything. If the medical profession wants to help—help that right constructively, instead of futilely, and quite pointlessly, trying to block it. The simple fact remains; if you can't help a man—don't try to keep him from seeking other help.

The medical profession has a tough problem, however. Naturally, no M.D. would be an M.D. if he felt that a hex doctor's training was more effectively curative. How then can a commission of M.D.'s evaluate hex doctors as to whether they are intentional quacks, or experimenters sincerely trying a different approach to a problem that medical science hasn't yet solved?

How is Panic to be evaluated? It consists, essentially, of acknowledging that no known method is adequate, and that an unknown must be tried. Suppose that the unknown is applied, and that shortly thereafter John Brown is found free of cancer.

Now how do we evaluate that? That medical efforts applied previously had finally taken effect? That the Unknown—let's say it was laying-on-of-hands by a hex doctor—was the cause of the effect? That the change in his whole life-pattern that took place when he accepted the need for the Panic Experiment caused a change in some psychogenic factor that underlay his cancer?

The M.D. will reject the laying-on-of-hands; it isn't a universally repeatable experiment. It cannot be fitted into any framework of cause-effect logic now known. It isn't, and can't be made into, a teachable science.

It's an individual-vs.-group problem again. The individual hex doctor laid on his individual hands, and cured John Brown, individual. But what good does that do anyone else, if it isn't teachable? Understandably, John Brown isn't too concerned about that, just now; he's cured.

But there are other problems. There was an old doctor in Upper Michigan, years ago, who had his own mystic salve for wounds. (Not cancer.) Some weird gunk of his own. The local medical society tried several times to make him shut up practice, but didn't succeed. The salve was analyzed at the University of Michigan and rated worthless. People liked his salve, and claimed it helped on ulcerated sores. The medical society objected strongly, back in the '20s and '30s, because it was perfectly ordinary salve, except for some highly unsterile, foul-smelling mold he put in it.

By all that was then known, putting a mold in a wound salve was not only nonsense—it was unsanitary, and wrong. How were the doctors then to guess that the old boy had, somehow, accidentally stumbled on some high-potency antibiotic producer? Understandably, they were intensely irked that the old fool with his crazy salve was so well-regarded by patients who didn't know any better. To the best of their sincere and honest judgment, the salve was, or should be, a menace to the health of the patients. It contained nothing beneficial, to the best of their knowledge, and did contain something that was very probably—to their best knowledge—decidedly unsterile. They would have been dishonest if they had not maintained that, in their best judgment, the salve was a menace. Certainly no honest doctor, in his right mind, in 1930 would have suggested to his patient that smearing a blue-green bread mold on his wound would stop the ulcerative infection!

It just happened to be true.

That, in essence, is the problem of the cancer quack. It's complicated by the fact that, as has been demonstrated repeatedly at Lourdes and other shrines, in some individuals, for some unknown reasons, faith-healing of cancer does take place. If John Brown happened, for reasons unknown, to have developed enormous faith in "Dr." Johannus Q. Diddlewiddy, and Dr. Diddlewiddy gave him a series of injections of not-too-sterile salt water—John Brown could have been completely, thoroughly, and unarguably cured of his incurable cancer. Since present science looks to objective causes for observed events . . . how to evaluate Dr. Diddlewiddy's salt-water cure? Particularly if Dr. Diddlewiddy happened to be not a money-grabber quack, but an entirely sincere, however misguided, man? Suppose Dr. Diddlewiddy has that mysterious power of "laying on of hands"—which has been reported repeatedly—doesn't know it, and sincerely believes that his impure salt water is the curative agent?

Sure, the problem's tough. But it is *not* going to be banished by trying to rule out "cancer-cure specialists" by legal action. The W.C.T.U. tried to solve the problem of alcoholism by passing laws against alcohol.

The American Medical Association is going to get just about equally effective results in trying to legislate away the ancient human right to Try Anything when the panic situation arises.

Panic makes sense, then; legislating against panic action is faintly ridiculous, isn't it?

AUGUST 1956

One of the major faults I find with the "scientific approach" to problems is the powerful tendency to hold that that-which-is-known necessarily embraces all-that-is-possible. Stated in that form, of course, any scientist would immediately deny it; it's normally stated in reverse form—i.e., "nothing known can produce such effects, so it is clearly a hoax, misobservation, or fraud."

I've been interested for some years in watching the case of *Krebiozen*, a cancer-treatment that has been vigorously attacked by the AMA—as have all cancer treatments other than their accepted, standard procedures of radiation, surgery, and caustics. There's been a running battle for years between the doctors who have used the stuff and believe they have clear evidence it works, and the AMA people who have not used it and insist it doesn't work.

For a long time, the Krebiozen faction refused, or claimed to be unable to supply a purified sample of their material for AMA-sponsored analysis; they demanded that the AMA make what amounts to a biological assay test—i.e., run a standard double-blind test of the effectiveness of the remedy in actual cancer cases. In a double-blind test, neither the doctor nor the patient knows which individuals are getting the test-drug, and which are getting blank solutions; only a central computer has the number-correlations that finally match results with identification. This is the one type of test that assures that subjective factors will not influence either the patient's reactions, nor the doctor's evaluations.

The new drug laws—resulting in part from the thalidomide furore—finally made it possible for the AMA, working through the Federal Drug Administration, to force the Krebiozen faction to supply a concentrate of their material for chemical analysis.

Chemical analysis has many powerful tools these days; infrared spectroscopy shortly permitted identification. The infrared spectrum of the Krebiozen sample was shown to match, one-to-one, the infrared spectrum of a well-known protein component of muscle tissue—*creatine*. The effects of creatine being well known —none whatever—it was at once clear that Krebiozen could not have any useful effects, as the AMA had long maintained.

There is, it seems to me, just one slight hitch in that simple-minded conclusion.

I am prepared to supply an extremely effective herbicide which I can positively guarantee can be shown by the most careful chemical analysis to consist of extremely pure water. "Conductivity water," in fact—water so extremely purified that it does not conduct electricity. There will be less than 0.001 parts per million of impurity in it. And chemical analytical techniques haven't even started to get good enough to reach that level of analysis!

Which seems sort of contradictory, in view of the fact that certain impurities in water, present in concentration of about 10^{-15} are legally defined as making the water "impure." And I am not talking about radioactives, either—perfectly ordinary chemical compounds of stable elements.

My herbicide belongs to the same type-class; a concentration of 10^{-18} or so would be quite adequate to ruin a field of growing plants. Readily proven by biological assay . . . but some *ten orders of magnitude* beyond the reach of chemical analysis!

How? Well, starting with conductivity water, I need add only a very minute trace of a known crystalline material—tobacco mosaic virus. The resultant solution, sprayed on young tobacco plants, could do quite a job, couldn't it?

And the legal definition of impure water has to do with the permissible concentration of *bacteria coli* in the water. Anyone want to try to spot that quantity of complex protein by *chemical* analysis?

So Krebiozen contains creatine? Well, well . . . And what else does it contain? Probably some hydrogen oxide too, I betcha. Since it's extracted from horse serum, it's quite apt to contain a couple of oddments of metabolic processes. Horses being noted for their quantity of muscle tissue, the presence of a muscle tissue extract of no significance isn't too startling, really. And since the mighty powers of modern chemical analysis can't find anything else present, that proves that creatine is all that's there.

Look friends . . . I have a bottle of a nice clear solution that should improve the situation for chemists who think like that. They're free to analyze it to their hearts content . . . if only they'll drink it after they've "proven" it has nothing of any significance in it. Lessee now . . . we could load it with botulinus spores . . . or concentrated polio virus . . . or even anthrax spores; then we could let him boil it for an hour before swallowing it, and still the damn fool would have personal experience with the fact that the limits of his knowledge and talents are *not* the limits of reality.

I have no personal interest in Krebiozen; I do have an acute personal, as well as citizenship interest in the honesty of thinking of science and medicine.

Anyone in a field of medical-biological work who considers, even temporarily, that chemical analysis is adequate for the determination of an unknown remedy is inexcusably incompetent, dishonest, or muddleheaded beyond toleration.

To consider that spectrum identification is an adequate tool for such work is even further in the direction of fantastic—appalling! —irresponsibility. Obviously spectrum identification requires that the spectrum be already known. This is a way to analyze an *unknown* material?

One microgram of cobaltamine—vitamin B-12—is considered a reasonably adequate vitamin supplement for that material. If an adult consumes one kilogram of food, plus an additional kilogram of water in a day, the concentration of that vital cobaltamine is 0.005 parts per million in his diet. You will, maybe, find this with an infrared spectrum?

Cancer, it is currently believed, arises from cells whose growth-regulating mechanisms have gone wrong—somehow the DNA-RNA information has been altered disastrously.

It is currently believed that virus particles are more or less loose DNA fragments, wrapped up in a protein capsule.

It's quite conceivable that the ultimate answer to cancer would

be a highly specific virus that contained precisely the DNA codons that the cancer cells lacked—and attacked them, without,
of course, bothering normal cells at all. (One class of thing you
cannot learn is that which you already know. The cells that already have the codon information on self-restraint wouldn't
"learn" anything from such a virus; the cancer cells would.)

If someone prepared such a virus, and submitted a highly
active and adequate sample to the present AMA-FDA groups,
it's evident that it would be reported as "fully identified as a
solution of sodium chloride in water." Virus particles in normal
saline solution, concentrated to about 10^{-12} would be an extremely powerful solution . . . biologically!

Remember that it is inevitably necessary that I use analogies
which you, the reader, already know the answers to. If I handed
you an example, instead of an analogy, it would of course be
meaningless! I can, for instance, hand you an example-for-a-1935-
scientist, but it will be an *analogy* for you. Suppose I could borrow a time-transistor somehow, and slip back to the Bell
Telephone Laboratories, in 1935, and hand them a collection of a
few modern solid-state devices. Say a silicon diode rectifier, half
the size of a golf ball, rated at 150 amperes, 400 volts peak inverse.
(That would drive the power-supply division into a flying
frenzy!) And a grown-crystal audio-amplifier unit, with grown-in
solid-state resistors, capacitors and transistors, half the size of a
pea. A simple little semi-microscopic germanium diode detec-
tor, too, and perhaps be very generous and supply a couple of
the new silicon carbide lasers. ("You put in the juice here and
here, and the coherent beam of blue light comes out *here*.")

Let us now stand back and watch the chemists try analyzing
that stuff. That silicon rectifier, now . . . they'll find it's a single
crystal of pure silicon. They haven't got a technique good enough
to come close to guessing *how* pure. (None of their reagents, or
the water they're using to analyze it, are pure enough anyway;
the techniques for getting commercially usable quantities of conductivity water weren't developed until transistor work forced
them into use.) And since they can't come close to the purity of
the silicon, they can't possibly detect the doping impurity that
makes it work. They won't do it with a spectroscope, either—

partly because they don't know how to get a spectroscope clean enough to do any good! The "background noise" of contaminants in their reagents, their equipment, and the atmosphere they work in would conceal the doping impurity.

A large part of the work the Bell Labs did in the years after they did invent the transistor was concerned with developing techniques for getting clean tools, clean reagents, clean equipment, which made possible the modern transistor. It wasn't just the concept of the transistor they developed; Bell Labs had to develop a whole new chemical and industrial concept to make production possible.

"Zone refining" was one of those—a technique whereby already ultra-purified germanium, silicon, or other material could be super-ultra-refined.

Back around 1940, the people working with copper oxide rectifiers at Bell Labs and other electronics industry research centers, knew that copper from a certain area in Chile made the best copper oxide rectifiers. Montana copper wasn't as good, nor was African or Mexican.

Yeah—sure—everybody knows that copper is an element, and an element is an element, and where it comes from has nothing to do with the matter. And in the days before knowledge of the "doping" behavior of semiconductive materials was available, who knew that a small-fractional-part-per-million impurity could make a huge difference?

The labs had tried analyzing the Chilean copper; they were perfectly sure that there was *some* impurity present. But no technique known to science as of 1940 was able to detect it.

After the information was of no practical significance—copper oxide rectifiers having been entirely displaced by silicon and germanium diodes—techniques developed in transistor research made it easy to determine the impurity. Zone refining, for instance, can sweep all the impurities on a bar of germanium—or copper—down to one end, thus concentrating them neatly for analysis. But by then, of course, it had become a completely academic question. . . .

However, if someone says something like that business about

only Chilean copper being good for the device he's invented . . .
he almost certainly wins himself, right there, the "Strictly Crackpot!" label.

On the other hand, when the AMA and FDA proudly an-
nounce that they have completely identified a previously unknown remedy because they've identified the infrared spectrum
of one component . . . that, sir, is Science at Work!

Pardon me while I go back to Magic.

The magicians used to try something out before they decided
whether it worked or not.

JANUARY 1964

"CREATINE HAS NO KNOWN
PHYSIOLOGICAL EFFECTS."

The FDA's recent blast at Krebiozen as being "nothing but creatine" is of interest in view of the following item—a letter which
appeared in *Science* (17 November, 1964, p. 1113).

Pre-1962 Creatine sought.
We are seeking help in finding 50 grams of Eastman (Distillation
Products Corporation) creatine, catalog No. 951, purchased prior
to 1962. We have been informed that the source of the creatine
sold by Eastman has changed, and we find a different physio-
logical response from that formerly found in rats fed creatine.
Eastman has been unable to locate a supply of the earlier product
for us.

W. R. Todd, Department of Biochemistry,
University of Oregon Medical School, Portland.

Whether there has been an impurity in the old which is not in
the new, or vice versa, seems to be undetermined at this point.

But of course, both lots were sold as being "nothing but creatine."

The rats appear to have considered otherwise.

SEPTEMBER 1965

LOUIS PASTEUR, MEDICAL QUACK

"Be not the first by whom the new are tried,
Nor yet the last to lay the old aside."

Essay on Criticism
Alexander Pope

My recent editorial on "Fully Identified," concerning the FDA's press splash that Krebiozen had been "fully identified" as creatine brought in a lot of letters, and a lot of phone calls from people acutely interested in Krebiozen.

My point in the editorial had been single, simple, and specific: whether Krebiozen was or was not useful in treatment of cancer I did not know—but that the FDA's press release was exceedingly bad science, anyone who took the trouble to study the matter a little could readily see. It was a great piece of publicity work—all about the summer student who tracked down the spectrogram . . . charts and whatnot—got a big splash in *Life* and the newspapers. As publicity stuff, that was a Grade A piece of work. Having some familiarity with the art myself, I recognize a real artist's touch.

That doesn't make it science. I've learned since that it not only wasn't science, it wasn't even honest reporting. The sample of Krebiozen the FDA reported on, according to data published in the "Congressional Record," was light tan in color, and fluorescent under ultraviolet light. Creatine is snow-white, and not fluorescent. The fact that any sophomore chemist would immediately recognize that an impurity was present seems not to have reached the scientists of the FDA's staff.

My objection was simply and solely to the specifically non-scientific methods being used in the name of Science in that instance. The letters I got—and the telephone calls—were from individuals who had a very different problem.

One typical one was from an electronic engineer in his late

thirties. Four years ago he was operated on for cancer of the intestines; a year ago the cancer recurred. The doctors who examined the situation then told him that it had spread, and was inoperable; they could offer him only palliative medication that would prolong his life, and reduce the pain.

Six months ago, he started taking Krebiozen. The pain left, and the tumor shrank away.

The FDA has now announced that they have "determined" on the basis of "scientific evidence" that Krebiozen is ineffective because it is "nothing but creatine," and, therefore, have ruled that he cannot have Krebiozen any more; it will be illegal to sell it.

So what's his situation? In effect, the FDA is telling him to go back on a "morphine diet," and toddle off to the grave like a good little man, and stop messing around with these unorthodox treatments that aren't good for him.

I would like to raise a question here: Is it ethical for a group of men who can offer him no hope whatever, to deny him the right to *try* a remedy of which they do not approve?

For that matter, is it ethical to take from a man who is recovering, a remedy which *he believes* is curing him?

Any doctor knows that there is such a thing as a "placebo effect"; that a completely inert material, which the patient believes in, can produce an effect when a biologically potent material, which the patient distrusts, will not.

One example of that: an arthritis patient, when cortisone first began to become available, had been begging her doctor to let her have some. The doctor told her it was hard to get, but that he had a new remedy that was supposed to be almost as effective, and he would start trying to get cortisone for her as soon as he could. In the meantime . . .

He did, in fact, have cortisone on hand. He did, in fact, give her cortisone injections. For four weeks, she was getting cortisone, while the doctor told her he was trying to get some for her. She showed no improvement or reaction to the "substitute"— which was in fact cortisone. The fifth week, with great showmanship, the doctor told her the cortisone had finally come in, showed her the cortisone ampule with its label, filled a hypodermic with sterile saline solution, and injected that.

She showed immediate and dramatic improvement on the sterile salt-water therapy.

That phenomenon is one of the things that makes evaluating therapeutic techniques somewhat more difficult than measuring a voltage, or weighing electrons or the companion star of Sirius.

The field of medicine is one area where subjective reality and objective reality directly interact; they cannot be separated. The term "psychosomatic" has been sort of dropped, and a new term not including the offensive "psycho" term substituted; they are now called "stress-associated diseases," or "stress-associated" conditions.

Every indication is that cancer is a stress-associated disease.

With the above data in mind—is it ethical for any group of men to deny Krebiozen to an individual in the spot my telephone caller was in?

The problem in this whole area of medical therapy is acutely emotional; that is why such exceedingly bad "science" as the FDA's Krebiozen report keeps showing up. It's long been known that human beings tend to count their successes carefully, and forget their misses—and to forget the other guy's successes, and count all his misses. The more intensely emotional the situation, the more powerfully that tendency is manifested.

And medicine is the field where emotional forces are on a full par with objective forces. The problem is that that applies not only to the patient—*but to the doctor as well.*

Let me put it this way: Consider two ideals of what a doctor should be.

1. The patient wants a doctor whom he can trust not only as a wise and learned man, but as a friend in his time of trouble, a man with genuine sympathy and empathy—a man who is personally and genuinely concerned for his patient's welfare. Simply —a doctor should be a man who *cares* what happens to his patients.

2. The theoretical ideal of a doctor is a man who is highly trained, skilled, and intelligent, a man who thinks coolly and objectively at all times, in all emergencies, who does not get flustered, and whose judgment is not warped by emotional factors.

Look those two ideals over carefully—and you'll see at once that they are mutually exclusive. If a man cares—then he is influenced by emotional factors. If he is cool and objective—then he is not warmly sympathetic. Moreover, he'll make a poor doctor —because the emotional factor is a critical factor in the therapy of the patient, and the "cool, objective thinker" specifically withholds emotional warmth.

Now anyone—in or out of the medical profession—will agree that there are always some cynical men who become doctors as a way of making a high income, and getting high social status. And that such men do not deserve the title "doctor."

And if you think about it carefully, you'll recognize that the cynical, money-hungry, status-seeking M.D. will be coolly objective in his evaluations, his judgment will not be warped by emotional involvements. He will, in other words, closely approximate the logical-theoretical ideal of what a doctor should be . . . and that no one wants for a therapist himself!

Such a doctor is like a highly skilled mercenary soldier; he may be more skillful, more effective in the battle, than a true patriot dedicated to the cause. He fights coolly, effectively, and skillfully—but entirely without loyalty or dedication. He wants his side to win, because that's the side that will pay him for his work.

The man who is dedicated to a cause is, by definition, emotionally involved in it; his evaluations of that cause will not be objective. His judgment will be warped by his involvement.

A parent can not judge his child objectively; an Englishman can't evaluate England's policies in the world objectively, any more than an American can evaluate ours objectively. And a true, dedicated healer-physician can not judge medicine objectively.

Yet each of those—parent, Englishman, American and doctor— will be sincerely and honestly convinced that he is being objective.

And emotional involvement will make a well-trained, highly-logical scientist become completely unreliable and unscientific.

It's long been known that it is very unwise of a doctor to treat his own family; his hopes and fears—his emotional involvements —will warp his judgment under precisely the circumstances he most ardently wants to be most effective. It is not ill-intent that warps his judgment, but excess of deep concern!

Strangely, a doctor could be more accurate in his evaluations when treating a man he despised than in treating his own wife or child.

Only the money-hungry status-seeking cynic—the medical mercenary with high skill and no dedication—can remain objective!

There's intense emotion on the part of the patients, too, of course; medicine is a matter of life and death, of health and crippling, of successful living or agony and slow death. No other success can have much value, if health is lost.

This leads to another aspect of the problem, one that affects the medical mercenary as acutely as the dedicated doctor. In our current society, the concept of the Welfare State and Security has spread to a quite unsane degree. People now demand Security against Death and ill health.

The Declaration of Independence was—as it openly states—prepared primarily as a propaganda document. It asserts that Life, Liberty and the Pursuit of Happiness are inalienable rights; this is a self-evident falsity. If they were inalienable, no one would ever have to defend them. The one truly inalienable right is the right to *try—with no guarantee whatever of success.* You have an inalienable right to *try* to live, to *try* to be free—but today, the Welfare-Security concept has promoted the concept that we should *have* those, that we should be guaranteed success in our efforts.

And—that a doctor should guarantee that there is no risk in his therapy.

The rise of that concept has led to more and more extreme malpractice suits. It used to be that if a woman was unfortunate enough to bear a Mongoloid idiot baby, she and her family would accept it as one of the risks of life and the life-process of reproduction.

Now they sue the doctor.

It used to be that if someone were unlucky and seriously injured in an automobile accident, they sued the driver who nearly killed them.

Now they sue the doctor who stopped by the roadside and rendered first-aid treatment.

Under this philosophy, Jesus' parable of the Good Samaritan would have wound up with the injured man suing the Good Samaritan for restoration of the money the thieves took.

This constitutes a problem for the medical-mercenary as well as the dedicated doctor. Such suits are always based on "second-guessing" the doctor on the job. "If he hadn't done . . . then I believe that . . ." is easy for the second-guessing doctor to say. (And a doctor willing to second-guess under those circumstances is always findable; the unskilled as well as undedicated medical mercenaries specialize in that as a source of income.)

Some human beings are violently allergic to wheat, strawberries or bee stings. This does not prove that wheat, strawberries or bees are deadly, lethal, evil, intolerable, terrible things to be eliminated from the world. It proves that the guy's unlucky in that *he* doesn't fit the world very well. It's not the world's fault— it's his fault.

But the man who turns up allergic to penicillin, thalidomide, MER-29, or some other new and highly useful drug—*he* sues the doctor.

It's a refusal on the part of patients to acknowledge that the act of living involves risk—and he *has* to accept that risk. Oh, no! Not under the Welfare-Security philosophy! He feels he is *guaranteed* success and health.

All of these factors focus in on the problem of new therapies, new drugs—plus one more.

Back before Pasteur discovered germs, Semmelweis discovered a 99.9% successful method of stopping childbed fever. There was a hospital in Vienna, one half of which was run by nuns, and the other half by doctors. The incidence of childbed fever in the doctor's half of the hospital at times ran as high as 90%— nine out of every ten young women who came in to have their babies died of infection. The nuns had a far better record.

The doctors didn't observe that fact particularly; the women of Vienna were acutely aware of it, however. (The human tendency to count your hits, and forget your misses—while the women observed the misses a lot more actively.)

Semmelweis, studying the situation, came to the conclusion that the difference was that the doctors, as part of their routine, performed autopsies on the dead women; the nuns did not. Semmelweis came to the completely false, crackpot notion that it was the odor of death on the doctors' hands that transmitted the disease. It just happened that he picked, as his deodorizer, chlorine water. It did indeed deodorize the doctor's hands; also, quite unknown to Semmelweis, it was an extremely powerful antiseptic —the concentration he used would kill anything.

At that time—about a century ago—it wasn't customary to wash the hospital sheets very often, either—until Semmelweis detected the "odor of death" there, too. "Wash 'em! And use chlorine water!"

The death rate from childbed fever among Semmelweis' patients dropped from about 90% to 0.9%.

For this, Semmelweis was thrown out of the hospital by the other doctors, and violently attacked and harassed by the medical profession of Europe.

Why? Because of a certain emotional factor involved.

His work—his absolutely unarguable and shocking success—said "Doctor—healer!—*you* killed those young women. *You* killed them with your dirty hands. They didn't just 'happen to die'; *you killed them!*"

Semmelweis was, of course, a dedicated healer; he could not endure standing idly by, so he was very busily spreading the word to laymen—telling them not to let a doctor examine a woman unless he scrubbed his hands in chlorine water.

There's the old saying "What you don't know won't hurt you." With respect to objective factors, that's obviously false. With respect to emotional things, however—it's true. So long as a doctor could hold off from his own mind the realization that it truly *was* his unclean hands that did it—then he did not have the grinding agony of regret.

Of course, the medical-mercenary type wouldn't have such a reaction; they could be more objective, less emotional. They never had cared particularly anyway—and Semmelweis' techniques would assure them of more patients. (Except for that damnable chlorine water; scrubbing in the stuff ruined the hands and devastated the fingernails. But it might presently be found that a dilute perfume—diluted with the usual 70% alcohol solvent —removed the odor of death just about as effectively.)

Of course, the Philosophical Logical Ideal doctors wouldn't resist Semmelweis' new idea; they wouldn't react to emotional factors like regret or remorse or guilt. And such men wouldn't be doctors worthy of the name, either.

In summary, then, the true, dedicated doctor, by the very nature of his dedication, cannot be an objective scientist; he cannot evaluate new proposed therapies objectively because he is dedicated—has a loyalty to his art. And he will have powerful emotional blocks against learning such lessons as Semmelweis taught, which show unmistakably that the doctor himself has been killing his patients through ignorance.

On top of that, the modern attitude that the patient has a right to perfect security, puts the doctor under terrific pressure to refrain from *any* new therapy.

Now let's consider for a moment what's meant by a "quack" in the medical field.

The usual charge is that a quack is someone who uses an improper treatment, one which does not help, or actually injures the patient, while inducing the patient to pay for this mistreatment, and keeping the patient from going to a licensed doctor and getting the treatment he needs. That a quack is in the business solely to make money at the expense of suffering humanity.

Now any time A disapproves of B emotionally, he'll attribute B's actions to some generally demeaned motivation—"just for money" being the most common, with "just for his own pleasure" being runner-up.

Let's be a bit objective about this business of what a quack does. Suppose a man, calling himself Dr. Jones, treats a patient who has a lethal disease, and uses a method that he knows for a positive fact will not save the man's life. He charges fees, and sees to it that the patient doesn't go to any other therapist—just gives him some drugs that do not save him, but let him die slowly.

That set of actions fulfills exactly what the AMA accuses those awful, nasty, wicked quacks of doing.

It is also precisely what an AMA doctor does when he treats a leukemia patient; he *knows* that the standard treatments for leukemia do not work, do not save lives. Leukemia, treated by AMA methods, means death.

The AMA, moreover, does everything in its power to make it impossible for the victim to get treatment from any other therapist who *might* be able to do better, and most certainly couldn't be less effective.

The patient will, moreover, wind up broke, and his family in debt—a charge constantly leveled against those wicked quacks! —by the time he dies.

But this is not quackery, of course.

Why not? Because the doctors know they are doing their best, with the best of intentions—which is strictly an emotional statement.

How about an unlicensed non-M.D. who does his best, with the best of intentions—despite the AMA's convictions that he *must* be evil—and actually does better than the AMA's best?

Oh . . . I see. That never happens, huh . . . ?

Well, it hasn't yet been proven for leukemia . . . but how about that unlicensed non-M.D.—that charlatan, that fraud, who'd gotten crackpot ideas from studying silk-worms and wineries, no less!— who started treating human beings for rabies? That chemist, with only half a brain, Louis Pasteur?

Or how about that licensed M.D. charlatan, expelled from the hospital and the medical society—Semmelweis?

Or take a few other notorious quacks like Lister—who was most violently attacked for his temerity in opening the abdomens of living patients. (Ethical doctors of the time never opened the abdomen until after the patient died.) And Ehrlich, another chemist, who invented the concept of chemotherapy.

Every time someone outside—or even inside!—the field of medicine brings up a break-through discovery, he'll be labeled a quack. The field is too emotional.

He'll be charged with being a fraud, a charlatan out after money, a blood-sucking leech.

Hoxsey had something that appeared to help cancer cases. Standard Operating Procedure of the AMA is to deny it, and charge the innovator with being a fraud, a charlatan, a money-seeking leech . . .

Hoxsey sued the AMA, Dr. Morris Fishbein, their President, and the Hearst newspapers which published the statement, for libel. He won the case.

Whether his cure actually worked or not was never investigated; the AMA flatly refused to test it.

But the question of whether Hoxsey was a charlatan, a deliberate fraud, *was tested*. He wasn't. Whether he did, in fact, have a cure has nothing whatever to do with whether or not he was a fraud; a fraud is someone who knowingly and deliberately misstates facts. Hoxsey had excellent evidence to lead him to the conclusion that his cure worked; that fact alone is complete and final proof that he was not illy or fraudulently motivated.

Look—let's be objective. Hoxsey may have been wrong—but the AMA doctor who treats leukemia by methods *he knows* will not save the patient's life seems to me in a damn poor position to call Hoxsey a quack. Hoxsey didn't *know* he couldn't save lives, and did, in fact, have a lot of reason to believe he could. And Hoxsey wasn't urging the passing of laws that would prevent the victim of such a disease from even trying to get help elsewhere.

As I say—this whole business is a mass of tangled, boiling, violent emotions. Does intent count in such matters? How much should it count? How do you know a man's real intentions? The medical mercenary intends to make money and gain status—and he may be the most highly skilled, highly competent surgeon in the city. Another man may be deeply dedicated, completely sincere . . . and unfortunately just not really bright. He lacks the spark that makes real surgeons. So here is one man with the "evil" intention of making money, the medical mercenary, and another who has the best of intentions. And—should we say the incompetent man is a better doctor?

I propose a new approach to this problem.

Let's license quacks. We'll make it wide open; anyone whatever, with no qualifications required save only that he be over twenty-one, and never committed to an institution for insanity, can apply for and get a license to set up in business as a medical quack.

Here's why: If a doctor diagnoses a man and tells him "The disease you have will kill you within three months; there is nothing that we can do to save you. All we can do is give you drugs to ease your pain, and perhaps prolong your life a little," that man is unsane if he does not seek some other therapist. And a man does have an inalienable right to try to live; you may try to stop him, but you'll have to lock him up to prevent his trying to find someone who will offer him some hope.

The fact that there are conditions which can be diagnosed, but which can not be cured by medicine today—and there always will be, no doubt!—is the fundamental reason why there are, and always will be quacks.

A quack is a man who thinks he can help conditions medicine cannot help. A man like Louis Pasteur, treating the Russian victims of rabies with a new technique no doctor in Paris would touch—treating them at the risk of a trial for murder, if they died.

Not all quacks are evil men. And there is a definite place for quackery! The area where medicine is competent to diagnose, and helpless to cure. If medical science can't help—then by all that's honest and ethical, they should damn well acknowledge it, step aside, and let someone else try!

Try a witch doctor, a faith healer, a numerologist—try a herbalist, or a chemist with a theory, or maybe a nuclear physicist. When you have nothing to lose, and life to win—*try anything!*

And *don't talk about money!* Whenever emotions start running high—and they always do, everywhere, in medical problems!—the business of money charges gets thrown in as the triumphant "That proves they're wrong! They do it for money!"

Have you taken a look at a standard AMA hospital and doctor bills for a couple of months of cancer treatment, with death of the patient? Talk about money! See, that proves they're just doing it for the money, huh?

Drop that money nonsense out of the thing; it's a question-begging argument from start to finish.

On the patient's side, he has a right to try anything he chooses; the organized medical groups have no right to deny him the right to try.

But there's a doctor's side, too. We're going to license these quacks—but it will be strictly, publicly, and thoroughly understood that it's a matter of "When you choose to gamble—you can't whine if you lose your bet." The quack is absolutely immune to suits for malpractice. Legally declared totally irresponsible for any deaths, crippling, or disasters that may result from his treatments.

This is simply putting into formal, legal and publicly stated terms what exists in fact anytime a man goes to a quack; it is the patient's responsibility to choose his own quack—and to take his licking if he gets licked.

But this means that a licensed M.D., a qualified man with a new theory, a new therapy to try out can *also* take out a license as a quack. He can hang out his shingle as "Thomas R. Brown, M.D., Licensed Quack Specializing in . . ." whatever it may be he's researching.

This would give the doctor a chance to do experimental work, and get out from under that insane business of unlimited malpractice suits. If the patient insists on Security—he goes only to tried-and-true, standardized-technique licensed doctors. If he has a disease in which the standard therapies don't work—he can take his choice of being perfectly secure in his dying, or sticking his neck out and taking a chance on a new therapy.

There's a third side to this system though—Society as a whole. And Society as a whole will benefit enormously from a system of licensed quackery.

Quackery always has existed; it exists now—and it always will exist, for the reasons given above. Diagnosis always precedes therapy; diagnostic techniques will always exist before therapeutic techniques have been able to cure the newly diagnosed conditions. In that twilight zone, quackery exists.

Now, however, quackery is illegal—a hit-and-run business pretty largely. No undercover operation can keep good records, and what records it does keep aren't communicated.

Let's license the quacks . . . and *make them keep extremely careful records.* They'll be the most useful research records Mankind has ever assembled! Even if the quack himself doesn't learn anything, other men very well may, from studying the records. Now, the quacks are unlicensed, and, therefore, unlimited. (They aren't even limited to over twenty-one and no-recorded-insanity!) Licensed, they can be limited in a number of ways— but the ways *will not* include any requirement of degrees or previous training. Put on such limitations, and the unlicensed quacks will immediately pop up where their records won't be available, and their activities will be unrestrained. The only restraint will have to do with two matters of statistics:

1. Only patients diagnosed as having diseases or conditions which standard medical records show to be, say, seventy-five per cent or higher lethal under known treatments will be automatically free to go to a quack if they want to. If the disease or condition is nonlethal, and has a zero cure rate—some skin diseases for example—the patient can ask for and *must be given* a pass to present to a licensed quack. The patient, not the doctor must determine this—because patients who want to go to quacks and are denied the pass will supply a group to maintain unlicensed and unrecorded quacks. But it gives the doctor a chance to point out to a girl with a disfiguring and incurable skin condition that while a *quack* might cure it—he's also quite apt to kill her.

But . . . any quack caught treating someone who does *not* have such a pass loses his license, and gets jailed.

2. The statistics on the quack's records are studied periodically. If his death rate is higher than the death rate under standard treatment—he gets shut down. We want better, not worse, treatments!

The gain to the Society as a whole is that, by such a system, a huge number of things that might work can be explored with the full co-operation and free permission of the self-assigned human guinea pigs. No man *has* to go to a licensed quack; it's his decision to be a human guinea pig. And in the process, we can learn a great deal about a lot of things that don't work—and thereby eliminate duplication of that useless effort.

There's a lot of emotionalism tied up in that concept of the human test subjects, of course. Doctors, when fulminating against quacks, have horrid things to say about such things.

But dedicated doctors, knowing the importance and good intent of what they were doing, aren't so upset when doctors in a major New York hospital, inject live human cancer tissue into human patients without the knowledge or consent of the patients.

That's *different!* That was for a good purpose, and they knew what they were doing!

Actually, it's pretty clear, the definition of "quack" is "someone I believe to be dangerous, evil, destructive and unprincipled."

Trouble is—the term "quack" was—in their own place and time—violently hurled at many men we consider today among the greatest medical heroes. Jenner—Harvey—Ross—Lister—Pasteur—Ehrlich—Sister Kenny—even Roentgen, who didn't even try to practice medicine!

One very certain thing about the field of medicine: it is not, and never will be a field of objective science. It's too deeply dominated by emotional factors.

JUNE 1964

"THE LAWS OF THINGS"

There is one area where Science and Religion become rather completely confused. Now basically, a Religion has to do with the nonmaterial side of Man's being; it is rooted in Faith—belief rather than objective evidence—and deals almost entirely with Man's emotional and moral structure. Its truths are revealed by Prophets after introspection and revelations from God (or Gods).

There's one area where Science becomes almost inextricably entangled in Religion—that area of Science that seeks to deal with Man's nonmaterial self, with his emotions and morality rather than his physical self. Psychology is the study of the Psyche, or Spirit, or Soul.

I don't like to attack any man's religion—but when a should-be science acts on Faith in the Revelations of a Prophet without reevaluation . . .

I suggest that the Great Prophet Freud needs some reevaluation at a considerably deeper level than the minuscule modifications that are currently acceptable among psychotherapists.

Consider this: Dr. Freud did his early investigations, on which his great theories of the universal underlying drives in all Mankind are based, among (1) largely Jewish people in (2) Vienna, (3) during the most extremely prudish period of Western culture. That is, among a cultural enclave in the midst of a mid-European city, during the midst of a very unusually prudish cultural period.

From this he derived as the Great Basic of all Mankind's motivations, Sex, and as the central conflict of all people, the Oedipus complex.

Now it happens that in the traditional Jewish culture, the mother is a powerfully dominant figure in the home—in effect, the Jewish culture is matriarchic. And the period in which Freud's patients were oriented was known as the Victorian Period, because of the tremendous influence that Britain's great Queen exerted over the entire world of her time.

I cannot help wondering what great universal motivations Freud would have found if he had studied patients among an equally restricted group of the Polynesians of Tahiti, say. There, there are almost no sexual inhibitions.

Freud didn't discover that a motivation other than Sex existed until about 1918—when he discovered the Death Wish. (He'd begun getting patients who'd been through that form of hell known as War—men to whom Sex was a less immediate problem than staying alive.)

The old question "Which leg of a three-legged stool is the most important?" has a practical answer. "The one that's missing."

From the cultural peculiarities of the "Gay '90s," Freud discovered the "missing leg" of Sex, and decided that that was the One Fundamental Motivation of All Mankind Everywhere.

Wonder what he'd have discovered as the Universal Motivation of Mankind if he'd done his studies entirely among the Dobu Islanders? Their culture holds that paranoid efforts to murder your neighbors by black magic—"Every man a wizard!"—is the normal way of life. They are poor, unfortunate individuals who have become insane and actually trust other people! These would, of course, have been Freud's abnormal neurotic patients there.

It seems, at first glance, that Freud's insistence on Sex in the ultra-prudish period of the 1890s-1900s showed great intellectual courage, to so fly in the face of his culture.

That's somewhat open to question. Did he, actually, *attack* the beliefs of his period? Or did he, rather, support them? That is, remember that the prudes of the time held that Sex was the Source of All Evil and Awful things. And what Freud appeared to them to be saying was that Sex was the cause of insanity and neurosis —wherefore the most violent prudes could happily chortle "See! See! We *told* you Sex was Evil! Now you know we were right! The great Dr. Freud has *proven* that it's nasty Sex that causes insanity, just as we said all along!"

Be that as it may, doing his research on a cultural enclave, in a Central European city, during an exceptionally prudish period, he (surprise! surprise!) found that Sex was the Universal Underlying Motivation. Not until the terrors of World War I drastically altered the cultural orientation around him did he discover *any* other motivation!

As of 1890–1900, modern cultural anthropology was barely beginning to get rolling. The use of statistical methods in analysis in the living sciences had not yet been accepted. (Gregor Mendel had been completely rejected for trying to use mathematical methods—statistics—in biology only a short while before, and his analytical method hadn't yet been fully accepted.)

Of course computer technology, logic circuit equations, and concepts of negative feedback loops were still a half-century in the future.

The immense dominance of European culture over all others in the world of 1890 made a central European "know" that "lesser breeds without the law" had weird customs, but that those weren't really *human*—weren't really relevant to the Universal Laws of Human Psyches.

Another aspect of Freud's theories that were very acceptable in that period was that the motivational systems Freud discovered were unique to human beings; that animals didn't have those characteristics. (And that, of course, is appropriate to the Science of the Psyche, because everyone knows that only Men have Souls.)

Then there are immense areas of both experimental-physiological and intellectual-analysis that have been opened up since Freud did his work—which have not been integrated with Freudian concepts, nor used to check the validity of the Freudian ideas.

Information Theory didn't exist in the 1890s. No one had, then, studied the micro-structure of the nerve-message pathways in the nervous system. The nature and limitations of Logic and logical analysis weren't understood. (Goedel's Proof that showed that Logic could *not* solve all problems hadn't been developed.)

And, finally, as of 1900, of course, Freud's theories hadn't been tried out in practice on actual neurotic patients all over the world for half a century.

There are, in Freudian Beliefs, things like "Oral Eroticism."

Since *all* motivation must be either Sex or Death Wish, and Sex, of course, dominates, any observed behavioral phenomena must be "eroticism" of some sort. Freud observed that people like to put things in their mouths, to suck thumbs, soda straws, cigars, cigarettes, candies, et cetera, and to show acute interest in their mouths. Since Sex and only Sex underlies motivation, this is, obviously and inescapably—unless you escape Freud—Oral Eroticism.

Of course, Freud wasn't aware of the violent psychic disturbances that result from sensory deprivation. The experiments hadn't been made at that time. Put a man in an environment where he can neither hear, see, feel, smell, touch, or taste anything—and within hours he begins to have hallucinations, becomes aware that his mental processes are disintegrating into uncontrollable unreality and madness. Sensory mechanisms need sensory inputs of some sort to fulfill their functions—and to stabilize the normal reality-checking motivation that real human minds actually have.

Now the mouth happens to be one of Man's primary sensory organs—and a very complex one indeed. It's the primary center of taste—and is, in addition, an acutely sensitive tactile organ, surpassing in that respect even the sensitivity of the fingers.

It is, also, the one and only Input to the Organism for solid or liquid substances. Small children frequently experiment with solid-substance inputs into the ears or nose, but usually learn quickly and painfully that those are *not* input stations.

But since Freud had no knowledge of Information Theory, or sensory deprivation experiments, and had the Great Revelation that all men everywhere always had Sex as the One Motivation, naturally it *had* to be Oral Eroticism.

Another one of Freud's Great Revelations was that there existed a Subconscious Mind, and it was conflicts between the Subconscious Mind and the Conscious Mind that led to neurotic compulsions.

Kant, some while earlier, had used the term "Categorical Imperative" instead of "compulsive or repressive"; the essential process was recognized in either case. For Kant, this "categorical imperative" was caused "by means of a function."

And Kepler, in stating the laws of planetary motion had recognized that there was gravity and inertia; Newton's great advance was to give precise *mathematically defined* expression to the Functions by means of which the planetary motions were imperatively determined.

Freud repeated Kant's observations in somewhat different wording—but without the sort of increased precision that Newton added to Kepler's realizations.

For some five thousand years of record preceding Freud, too, there had been recognition of the *ka, psyche, spirit, geist, soul* or whatever the local time-and-place term might be as a part of Man that was immaterial, analogous to the mind, but was not the same thing as mind.

Freud gave it a new name, but there was little change in the realization that this *psyche* was able to exert powerful and, at times, compulsive force over the mind of man.

Freud's greatest—and real—contribution probably was the specific, solid statement that the subconscious compulsions *were genuinely compulsions;* that an individual *could not* resist them— that it wasn't "unwillingness" or "stubbornness" or "weakness" that caused an individual to yield to the compulsions. That the psychotic paranoid who murdered a dozen neighbors due to his compulsions was no more able to resist that internally-generated pressure, than a martyr was able to choose *not* to be martyred by renouncing his beliefs.

The Ego, the Id, and the Super-Ego might also be named with somewhat older terms as the Mind (Ego) and the Conscience (Super-Ego) while the Id is perhaps a confusion of two other factors—the ancient instinctive wisdom of the race, and the third-factor effect of the interaction of Mind—which is logical and present-time based—and Conscience—which is acculturation, and neither logical nor present-time based.

Actually, of course, large parts of Conscience-acculturation agree one hundred per cent with large areas of the ancient racial instincts. In such areas, naturally, the culture claims that it, and it alone is the source of those Great Good Ideas. Where acculturation and racial wisdom disagree, naturally the culture insists that *that* is "nothing but evil old instincts which must be suppressed."

When conscience-acculturation demands the logically impossible, or irrational, naturally there's a conflict between it and Mind. (But acculturation will never acknowledge that *it* is wrong!)

However, we're dealing here, quite obviously, with the area of Morality—which Religion has always claimed for its own. And, of course, with most intense emotional areas—which have, from the findings of anthropologists, been the province of the witch-doctor-priest for at least two hundred thousand years.

Whether you say you are working with a man's Super-Ego or say you're treating his Soul is a distinction of verbal noises—unless you can define the difference in clear, functional terms. And if you claim that psychoanalysis is a Scientific Approach, rather than a priestly-witch-doctor method, that claim, too, needs some specific, functional definition.

It does appear though, that a "Scientific Approach" stemming from the revelations provided by one man, who derived his great basic realization of the Universal Motivation of All Mankind by studying a cultural enclave, in a central European city during an exceptionally prudish era, needs considerable reevaluation.

I can't help wondering what great revelations of fundamental human emotional structure would have come from Freud if he'd grown up among, and worked with, Dobu Islander patients. Sex being uninhibited among the Dobu Islanders, it wouldn't have appeared as the critical "missing leg"; whether he'd have called their culture of mutual murder motivation a death-wish culture or a security-seeking culture I can't decide. But on observing that men like to use their mouths—Kipling had made that observation before Freud!—a Dobu Island Freud would certainly not have spoken of "Oral Eroticism." "Oral Morbidity" possibly, or perhaps "Oral Security-seeking."

Naturally, I'm ever so much wiser than Freud on these things; hindsight is *sooooo* much more perceptive than foresight. Any high-school kid today is wiser than Aristotle, too. I've got a slightly unfair advantage consisting of two generations of world-wide efforts by anthropologists, archeologists and historians, plus the immense amount of work done by cyberneticists, Information Theory analysts, the space-scientists working on sensory deprivation—and the statistics of what's actually happened with patients treated with psychoanalysis during the last half-century.

My objections are not to Freud; he was a genuinely sincere and highly important philosopher of the mind.

My objections are to the Freudians—who have the same half-century advantages I have, and haven't adequately used them. Freud *didn't* know about Information Theory and sensory deprivation effects; he *didn't* have the data of a half-century of cultural anthropology to use in studying out the true, universal-to-Mankind motivations.

The modern Freudians *do* have that data.

Why don't they use it—when they also have the data *from their own statistics* that the recovery rate among psychoanalytical patients is not significantly different from the recovery rate among untreated patients?

Statistics on the recovery rate among patients treated by which doctors are somewhat hard to come by, of course. But the reports from cultural anthropologists indicate that perhaps the witch doctors have significantly better therapy techniques.

The greatest improvement in psychotherapy since records have been kept seems to have come about since the adoption of a physiological approach, thanks to learning from the Hindu herb doctors that tranquilizer substances exist.

It is, of course, improper to attack a man's religion; with the witch doctors, we would be dealing with the native religion.

I hope I have not, in this discussion, attacked anyone's religious faith.

JUNE 1965

LOGIC

I've had an opportunity to learn a little about a project now under way at the Harvard Computer Lab; the men engaged in it do not, probably, have the same opinions about it that I have formed. We'll find out later whether my hunches regarding it are valid.

I have a feeling the job now started will snowball for the next century or so—and that they have started on the most important basic project Man has ever tackled.

They're studying the problem of teaching a computing machine to translate English to Russian, and Russian to English.

It's my belief that, in the process, they will solve about ninety per cent of Mankind's social, psychological, economic and political problems. The computers won't solve the problems—but they'll force the men working on them to solve them.

Reason: You can NOT say to a computer "You know what I mean . . ." The computer would only reply, "No. Define 'you.' Define 'know.' Define 'I.' Define 'mean.' Operation-relational processes regarding these terms not available."

All right, friend—go ahead. Define "I." Define it in terms of function and relationship to the Universe. Define it in terms of characteristics of process and program the steps the computer is to take in interacting this concept "I" with the operational program steps meant by the concept "know." Just do that one, single little thing, just define that one pair of terms—and you'll resolve about seventy-five per cent of all human problems.

Korzybski was a piker. He tried to teach human beings, who have built-in automatic self-programming units. They may not be perfect, but they work with incredible efficiency.

Try teaching a computing machine what you mean by some nice, simple term like "food." There's a good, basic, simple idea— an item basic to the most elementary understandings of life processes, politics, sociology, psychology and economics. This is one that must be included, obviously.

Anthony Oettinger, one of the men working on the project, explained part of the problem very neatly and completely by telling of one phase of the difficulty. Suppose we take a common English saying, and translate it into Chinese. Now if translation were perfect, we should be able to retranslate to English and recover the original phrase. Actually, in one instance, the retranslation yields "invisible idiot." Guess what went in originally! It's a perfectly understandable result; after all, something that is invisible, is out of sight—and an idiot is one who is out of mind. It could equally have come out "hidden maniac" or "distant madman."

Translation cannot be done on a word basis; we don't use words, actually, but concepts. Translating word-by-word would be only slightly more rewarding than transliterating letter by letter. The Russian alphabet is different from ours; that doesn't mean that transliterating yields English. Neither does a word-for-word substitution, save in the simplest level of statement.

The Chinese-English saying translation above indicates the real difficulty—and one that General Semantics hasn't adequately recognized, I feel. Actually, in communicating with each other, we seek to communicate *concepts;* concepts are complex structures of many individual parts assembled in a precise relationship. If someone asked a chemist for sugar, and the chemist delivered a pile of carbon and two small flasks of hydrogen and oxygen—everything necessary for sugar is present, but it's not sugar.

Let's consider "food" a moment. Presumably we are seeking to achieve sane translations of sane human thinking from our computer. Under these conditions should we teach the machine to consider that human flesh is to be considered "food"?

Yes. A sane man must realize that his flesh is food—otherwise he would make the mistake of swimming in shark-infested waters, or ignore lions and other major carnivora.

Is wood "food"?

Yes; an engineer must realize that fact when he considers

constructing buildings. Otherwise he would neglect the possibilities of termite damage.

Is steel "food"?

We must so instruct the computer; otherwise it could not translate "We must have steel scrap to feed our hungry furnaces."

Very well, gentlemen, what *do* you mean when you consider the concepts in "foods," "feed," and "eat"? *Define your terms!*

The sociologists and psychologists have long maintained that mathematical methods are not applicable to human problems. Not until the terms in which human problems are discussed have been defined operationally, certainly.

Teaching a computing machine, a machine that will invariably do precisely, but only, what you did-in-fact instruct it to do will be a most humbling task. In the course of doing that job, I foresee the collapse of every human philosophy, the harsh winnowing of every human falsity, every slightest quibble, self-justification, or rationalization.

When a man is seeking to induce another man to agree with him, to learn his ideas, he can hold "he is stubborn; he refuses to understand me because he hates me." Or "He is too stupid to learn!"

When a man seeks to teach a computer . . .

Computers are not stubborn. If it is stupid, it is the failure of the man to perfect his handiwork, and the failure reflects inescapably to its source in Man. If it acts in a foggy, confused manner—Man made the mistake, and he must correct it. It's his mistake; responsibility cannot be assigned elsewhere.

Man, in trying to teach his tender and precious beliefs to a computing machine, is inviting the most appallingly frank and inescapable criticism conceivable. The computing machines won't solve human problems for us—but they'll force men to a degree of rigid self-honesty and humility that never existed before.

I can imagine some philospher, some psychologist, or some physicist coming spluttering to the computer lab, demanding that the nonsensical answers so blatantly in disregard of the facts-as-he-believes them be corrected. "Out of the way; let someone who knows something about this field teach this machine a few realities!"

Three weeks later, a haggard and vastly humbled man would come out, his fine structure of beliefs in tatters—and possessed of a realization of his own need to learn a few *real* realities.

I have heard psychologists use the term "ego," the terms "id" and "identity." I've looked, with some interest, in an Encyclopedia of Psychology; there is no entry under any one of those terms, no effort, even, to define them.

Have you ever sought a definition of "distance" as used in physics? It's one of the three fundamentals of the CGS system—and has no definition whatever. *Define your terms,* the computer relentlessly demands. The mathematician has no definition for "quantity" or "distance" either. Cantor has proved mathematically that any line segment has as many points—aleph null—as any other line, however long or short, or as any plane. Then define what you mean by "greater than" or "less than"! Until you do, the whole structure rests on "You know what I mean . . ."

The computer does *not* "know what you mean." Define it!

A while back I ran a faulty "syllogism" going, essentially, "Biology holds no organism can live in a medium of its own products. Communism holds a man has a right to what he produces. Therefore, Communism won't work." It was thrown in as a deliberate inducement to thinking and questioning of terms. Most of those who answered—some quite angrily, incidentally!—held that the flaw lay in the misuse of the terms "products" and "produces."

There's a flaw all right—but that's not it. The computer would have spotted it immediately; only we humans have difficulty in finding it.

The products of an organism are quite artificially divided into "products" and "by-products" and "waste products." As industry long since learned, a waste product is something we haven't learned a use for yet, and a by-product is a misleading term. What is the product of Street & Smith Publications, Incorporated, for instance? Street & Smith, like the National Biscuit Company, assembles materials, packages them, and distributes them. Rumford Press, which prints this magazine, like the American Can Company, or Container Corporation, makes packages.

You hold in your hand a physical package, packed with word-structured concepts. You buy a thing of paper, ink, and metal and glue—just as you buy a thing of glass, metal and plastic when you buy a radio tube. In each case, the object is merely a package-structure for the function which you really desire.

Any organism will smother in *any* of its own products if present in excess; a waste product is one present either in excess of the usable amount, or one which is not usable.

Any organism—including the organism known as a "state" or "nation"—will smother in an excess of its own ill-regulated and ill-distributed products. The basic biological law is perfectly applicable to a state, or a society.

The flaw in the false syllogism is the one the computer would have spotted immediately.

"Define the term 'right'!"

This is the distributive term in the syllogism, and is so undefined as to be meaningless. The falsity of the syllogism is equivalent to that in "All men are human beings. Some human beings are mortal. Therefore all men are mortal." The flaw in that syllogism is the faulty distributive term in the second statement.

But when it comes to "right," human beings are very, very skittish indeed. They're too apt to find that some of their pet beliefs and personal preferences will be ruled out if they accept any hard, clean-cut definition of "right."

Since a machine has no rights to begin with, no beliefs, prejudices, preferences or foibles, it will most unkindly and uncompromisingly refuse to operate at all until you define what you mean by "right."

I have a deep conviction that a vastly humbled and chastened —but vastly improved!—humanity will result from the effort to teach a machine what Man believes.

The terribly tough part about it is that to do it, Man will, for the first time, have to find out exactly what he does believe—and make coherent, integrated sense of it!

LIMITATION ON LOGIC

From the strong response in letters received after the recent editorial on logic, I gather you like questioning the whole subject. Obviously, I do too. So . . . let's try another approach, and see if we can't find something somewhat different from either the A or non-A business.

Let's define *logic* as "one of the methods of rational thinking." Conventionally, "logical" and "rational" have been considered synonymous; evidently that's stretching the meaning of logic quite a bit, or else using an exceedingly peculiar definition that's based on the individual's viewpoint on the matter at a particular time and/or place. I suggest that there are several other methods of rational thinking, and that *neither* Aristotelian *nor* non-A is adequate—that, in other words, logic is necessary but not sufficient.

You can get some most peculiar effects from considering data that is true, and nothing but the truth. For instance, it is perfectly true that I habitually come from my suburban home into New York City floating about four feet off the ground. I don't come down to Earth—and that's a true statement.

The fact that there's a train between me and the ground is, however, the rest of the truth. Frequently the truth and nothing but the truth is a particularly vicious kind of lie, because it can not be disproven or attacked in any way. I could, for instance, get twenty or thirty witnesses to confirm my statement that I came into New York without once touching Earth, and no witness could be found who could testify otherwise.

Logic has been based on the use of high-probability data; actually, the concept "true" and "false" can be interpreted as "probability of truth equals 1.000" and "probability of truth equals zero." It's mighty easy to evaluate data when the data can be classified in that nice, easy, put-up-or-shut-up manner. A relay is either open or closed—provided the contacts aren't dirty, and haven't welded together. A man is either alive or dead—until we find out how to suspend animation. A star either is visible out there in space, or it isn't—unless it's one of an eclipsing binary pair.

The unfortunate fact of the Universe is that, as Information Theory shows, the real physical Universe contains noise, and always will contain noise. There is *no* statement of Probability 1.000, and *no* statement of Probability Zero—save in the non-physical system of theoretical discussion.

The interesting and necessary conclusion from that fact is that mathematics, like Euclidean geometry, does not apply to the real Universe; mathematics is a noise-free system, and therefore cannot be congruent with the real, noise-containing Universe. And there cannot ever be any *exact* science that is congruent with the real Universe. No computing machine can ever be built which is both constructed of real physical components, and is congruent with the system of mathematics; the machine can only be tangential to the field of mathematics, because it, being physical, must contain noise, while the system of mathematics does not.

One consequence of that is that any real physical computer will, inevitably, have breakdowns. The observed fact is that they do!

Now I have done a great deal of my thinking on the basis of inadequate data, inaccurate data, using as data the fact that there was a lack-of-data, and that the data-is-inadequate. In the field of logic, which hs been confined to high-probability data, that sounds like a prescription for "How to think in a sloppy and improper manner." It isn't. But it will get you into some highly frustrating arguments, since the method of thinking involved *is not accepted generally.*

Consider this: An ordinary silk thread cannot support the weight of an automobile. This is an easily demonstrated fact. I can prove, then, that this specific thread, #1, cannot do it. Neither can thread #2, which I can test and prove inadequate. Neither can thread #3, which likewise fails under test. Nor thread #4, #5, #6, . . . #n. You see, I have proven that there is not one single bit of evidence which you can show me that silk thread will support an automobile. I can break down every single piece of evidence you bring up. Not one of those one hundred thousand threads you brought up as evidence that silk could support an automobile would actually stand up on examination, and that proves that you cannot lift an automobile with a silk cable.

I suggest that, in addition to the standard, conventional logical argument, there is also a quite different thing—the *gestalt* argument. The argument in which there is not one single argument of any useful strength—but in which there are many, many lines of argument which, as a gestalt, are more powerful than any single argument could be!

This is argument based on barely significant data, improbable data, inaccurate or inadequate data—which is, none the less, a completely sound argument. In terms of probability, it can be put this way:

Suppose there are ten steps, a sequence of ten dependent events. Each individual step has a probability of 0.1. We can represent this as "if A, then (0.1 B):: if B, then (0.1 C):: if . . ." et cetera.

Now in such an event sequence of ten steps, the product probability of the tenth step will be 10^{-10}—one chance in ten billion.

The above argument is a logical argument—i.e., a one-line-of-development argument. But let's consider a gestalt argument on the same subject.

It's true that the probabilities are such that "if A, 0.1B" applies on one line of development. But it happens that there is also "if A, then (0.05A')" and also "if A, then (0.08 A")" and "if A' or A", then (0.5B)" applies. And in addition, there are several other sequences involving A-to-A'-A"-to-B and a lot of other routes. In addition, there are various crossovers from B to side-chains that also lead to C. In fact, careful investigation reveals that there are, actually, ten trillion different possible lines down the whole ten-event sequence, no one of them having a probability higher than 10^{-10}th—but the summated probability products turn out to have a value of 0.99!

Now a chain is as strong as its weakest link—because it's a single-line development. Logic operates on that principle, and a logical argument can be completely shattered by breaking any one link in the sequence.

But a cable doesn't have links; breaking any one strand does not break the cable. And a gestalt argument doesn't depend on any single link, or any single line of development. Like the fibrous construction so typical of the strength of living things, each line of development is independent, but interactive; it will not shatter under stress, but is capable of elasticity. It can't be handled very easily by a mathematical process, because it's a noise-filled system; it's so interactive that breaking one line of development interacts to put more stress on the other lines of development. Many times blocking of one line of development simply increases the probability of another, while at other times, blocking one decreases adjoining and subsequent probabilities.

Gestalt argument methods simply haven't been formulated, and can't, at present, be described in detail. We're stuck with that. But we must, also, recognize that logic is the truth, and nothing but the truth—but a lie, if we don't recognize that it is not the whole truth.

In addition to gestalt arguments based on multiple-channel low-probability developments, there is a third method of rational thinking that has not been adequately formulated, but evidently does exist; let's call it *analogic*. Since I can't formulate either gestalt rationality, nor analogic rationality, I can't derive a sharp distinction between them, and show where the boundaries are such that they do not overlap. But that there are two distinct nonlogical rationalities I think can be shown.

When aeronautical engineers work with models in wind tunnels they have to do some very tricky mathematics, based on some rather largely empirical formulas called the Laws of Models. If you build a full-size fuselage and wing system having exactly the form of the model that tested successfully—you'll have a Grade A flop. The engineers are forced, by practical considerations, to experiment with models—which are *analogous* to the full-scale ship they want to build, but *not similar* to it. The full-scale ship will *not* work right if its form is *similar* in the sense the term "similar" is used in geometry—having the same angles and length-ratios.

In making the transformation of dimension ratios, the engineer is using *analogic*; he is reasoning by analogy, in one of the very few areas where analogical reasoning has been sufficiently formulated to be acceptable.

Any logician will throw out as not legitimate logic an effort to use reasoning by analogy; it has been held for many years that analogic reasoning is not logical reasoning. But *analogic is rational!* The Navy researchers towing test hulls in the Navy's tow tank depend on the rationality of analogic. In actual everyday living and thinking we must depend on analogic—yet we cannot defend our analogic in debate because there has never been an adequate formulation of the Laws of Analogic. This doesn't mean that no such laws exist; it simply means that we haven't found them yet.

Yet all science is, actually, based on the use of gestalt rationality and analogic rationality, far more than on logic, when the matter is investigated. Logic is the result finally achieved by the preliminary use of analogic and gestalt thinking.

Cosmologists are studying turbulence in a small laboratory pool of water in an effort to better understand the interactions of spiral nebulae. They find that galaxies collide, sometimes, and show *viscous* characteristics. How can that be? If we could formulate analogic, we could study better the pool of water, the swirl of gas in a near-vacuum, the eddy-in-space that is an atom.

Stellar mechanics has been greatly helped by the study of a large pool of mercury metal in a strong magnetic field. But if we just knew the Laws of Analogic, we could do a lot better.

Logic is only one of the methods of rational thinking!

MARCH   1954

AN ORIGINAL POINT OF VIEW

THE DEMEANED VIEWPOINT

It is terribly hard to convince a man he's wrong, under the best of circumstances. But it's even harder to convince him thoroughly that he's wrong—when he isn't. Things like the old folk-superstition, anciently held by the peasants of Europe, that, if you get a bad cut, putting a few spider webs over it will stop the bleeding. It's terribly hard to convince them that that's a silly superstition.

It just happens that the alien protein of spider silk is both highly reactive—that's part of why it's sticky—and highly alien; it causes the blood platelletes to shatter and cause clotting almost instantly. The strong network of spider-silk threads then form an excellent framework for the clot to establish itself on. A freshly made spider web is usually quite clean, and is more reactive than an old one. Works much better than the kind of highly non-sterile cloths a peasant is apt to have around.

It is, by the nature of things, the inevitable fate of any great leader in thought to have a horrible time getting his ideas over to his fellow man. He's a great leader because he has brand-new and important thoughts—thoughts that are highly disturbing, too, since they mean the abandonment of older, less effective ideas, that have long been cherished. The inevitable consequence of that situation is that every great leader blows his top every so often about the asininity of Mankind, the stupidity, recalcitrance, and general no-goodness of thick-witted, non-thinking, stubborn Man. Galileo's original papers are, I understand, marvels of vituperative language, much of it unprintable in any modern book. Every great leader has had excellent reason to fulminate about the recalcitrance and stupidity of Man—on how Man rejects stubbornly those things that are wise and good and sensible, clinging leechlike to his pet superstitions, his pet emotional responses, and his beloved—and stupid—superstitions.

In the Eastern tradition, the Great Thinker simply retires into himself, thinks his own great thoughts, and lets those who want to take the trouble to learn come to him. The Western tradition puts the Great Man on the spot; if you're so darned smart, let's see you do something useful with your ideas! And the first useful thing you can do is teach me. If you can't do anything useful with your ideas—why should I supply you with useful food, clothing and shelter? Why should I spend my useful-to-me time listening to you?

This, too, has caused more than one of the West's Great Thinkers to blow his stack on the subject of "gross materialism." I suspect a certain undercurrent of resentment that the world wouldn't give him the gross material to eat that he found necessary.

Now perhaps it would be worth while to review this situation, and see whether the indictments of Mankind's stupidity, recalcitrance, et cetera, are justified. The West's brutally ruthless tendency to make Gerald Genius get in and pitch for his living— to make his wonderful ideas useful—has unquestionably been exceedingly hard on the dispositions of many great, and potentially great men. It's distracted them, and forced them to spend time earning a living that they would prefer to have spent working out their great ideas. It's certainly been a handicap to those men.

But . . . well, maybe it has been worth while, at that. The East tried it the other way; it may well be that they achieved some mighty spiritual triumphs—but that's going to be hard to determine in another couple of centuries, since the highly teachable Western concepts are rapidly flooding over and submerging the original Eastern concepts. (The Western concepts are more teachable, because about ninety per cent of the time of a Western genius had to be devoted to sweating out some way of getting his idea across. The result was that the great talents of first-order geniuses were channeled into developing teaching methods. It was darned hard on the geniuses—but the Race of Man had found a way to harness its greatest thinkers to the benefit of all!)

But I have a feeling that the result has also had its bad aspects; the Teachers have been teaching under violent protest. They've been teaching, all right, but with the boiling, colossal anger and resentment of truly tremendous personalities—and a lot of that angry resentment leaks through, too. The essence of its message is "Man is a thick-skulled, thick-witted, fumble-brained dope, who will learn nothing unless it is driven into his stubborn noggin with a bludgeon! And if he isn't bludgeoned into learning, he'd remain a stupid clod forever!"

These are the attitudes of a frustrated and angry genius, a Galileo who was far ahead of his time, a Copernicus, Newton, or a Plato's attitude. Their ideas were obvious to *them*—but they were geniuses, men of abnormal power and stature. Is it appropriate to condemn Mankind for not being made up entirely of top-level geniuses?

Naturally, the genius doesn't want to be lonely—he wants understanding friends. Sorry; the penalty of being out in front of the crowd is that there is no crowd with you.

Actually, the genius probably doesn't want to be a leader; he is simply trying to be what his nature makes him—and it makes him lonely because his nature is unusual.

Well—"A poor workman quarrels with his tools." If the genius wants to work with Mankind, he might, perhaps, do so more efficiently if he got over blowing his stack at their stupidity, and tried taking the viewpoint he so violently demeans—that they are *not* stupid. That they have a great, and very ancient wisdom. That the flash of genius can be flashing in the wrong direction. Hitler was undoubtedly a genius; so was Ghengis Khan and many another of Mankind's great geniuses-in-the-wrong-direction.

The trouble is that the great men have transmitted not only their very real and very great wisdom to the culture—they've also transmitted their anger at Man.

Since geniuses suffer most intolerably from Mankind's intolerance of new ideas, the culture has a great schism in its thinking; it insists that we must be tolerant—and is intolerant. Possibly things would work better if we acknowledged that Intolerance is a great, useful, and necessary thing—properly used. It's worth noting that three billion years of evolution has produced a human organism that is so intolerant that you can't tolerate a skin-graft from any individual . . . unless you happen to be a one-egg twin, in which case you can tolerate a skin-graft from your genetically identical twin.

Three billion years of evolution doesn't make nonsense; why is intolerance a good and necessary thing? I don't know . . . but I've a strong hunch we'd do a lot better with controlling intolerance if we first found out what it was meant to do, and how it was meant to be used. Most communities feel that it is wrong to tolerate a thief, pervert, or a sadistic killer. Let's try the demeaned viewpoint that Intolerance is a sound, necessary, and valuable function—in its proper place.

When the United States tried the experiment of Prohibition, it held "There is no place for a liquor seller." Since people do want liquors, there obviously is a place for liquor sellers. Denying this fact pushed the liquor seller underground, where he operated without thoughtful control. The result was very bad liquor, poisonous liquor, and uncontrolled distribution of liquor. Fortunately alcohol is one of the best antiseptics, so bacterial contamination of the liquor due to dirty handling didn't add to Mankind's woes. Just imagine what would have happened if it had been milk!

So long as we insist "There is no place for Intolerance in human thinking!" we are going to have Bootleg Intolerance—uncontrolled distribution, badly organized intolerance, poisonous intolerance. I have a hunch that if we tried that demeaned viewpoint, we might accept that Intolerance is a fine and necessary thing—and wind up with a lot less, much more sanely distributed.

Of course, the powerful and sweeping condemnation of Intolerance that is standard in our culture is an excellent example of a type of thinking that our culture sweepingly condemns— thinking in terms of categories and sweeping generalizations. Inasmuch as the culture itself teaches that we should think in those terms, and does so by example, while teaching that we should not do so in terms of preachments, I'm a little confused as to what the culture does believe. The culture *preaches* that you should not think in sweeping generalities—but the culture *does* think in precisely that manner. It's a "Don't do what I do; do what I say!" problem.

Possibly thinking in generalizations is another of those demeaned and suppressed concepts that need to be brought out of the Bootleg class. Since mankind does, and has for a long, long time thought in those terms, and has, somehow, managed to survive, maybe there is a modicum of validity to it that needs to be found. You can't get a man to give up an idea when it's sound and valid; you've got to find the area of its validity, acknowledge it belongs there—and then he'll be able to agree there are places it doesn't belong. But saying it doesn't belong anywhere, under any circumstances, doesn't get you far. So long as you insist on that attitude, you can't regulate it, channel it, or apply it where it does fit.

Let's try taking the demeaned viewpoint; assume that thinking in categorical terms *is* valid, and see how it could be used.

1. Juvenile delinquents tend to grow up and become criminals.

"Why, that's no way to judge a man! I have a neighbor who was a juvenile delinquent, arrested seven times, and almost sent to reform school. But he's a fine man—an engineer with a big job in an important construction company. You're thinking in categories, and you know that's not sound."

2. Individuals who have no fixed address, no family, and no fixed associations in any business tend to be untrustworthy.

"That's nonsense! I know a man who's a business organization consultant. He's a bachelor, and he has no fixed address, and naturally, in his work, changes from one business association to another rapidly. That doesn't mean a thing; it's just sloppy thinking."

3. Individuals who carry concealed guns are usually open to considerable suspicion.

"Oh . . . nonsense! I suppose you'd say that a detective was a crook because he carries a concealed gun!"

4. There is a tendency for social deviants such as criminals to take to flashy and extreme styles of dress.

"That would make most of the teen-agers I know criminals! You can't judge a man's character by his clothes, and you know it."

5. This individual was a juvenile delinquent; he has no family,

no fixed address, no business associations, is carrying a concealed gun, and is flashily dressed. I suspect he may be a professional criminal, and will take precautionary measures on that basis.

Perhaps the major trouble with the use of thinking-in-categories is that most people do too little of it—they don't use *enough* categories. Senator McCarthy evidently feels that one-time interest in a Communist-associated organization is adequate proof that a man is untrustworthy—though it happens that his other category-associations include twenty or thirty conservative political, economic and religious organizations. It isn't that categorical thinking is itself wrong—but that, like any good thing, it can be used wrongly.

If you have a piece of glass, and put a streak of lacquer on it that absorbs ten per cent of the transmitted light, you can't blacken it with that. But if you put thirty such streaks across the glass, and they all intersect at one point . . . it won't be black, of course, but it'll be awful darned dark looking.

Maybe the human race would get along a bit better if it didn't try to totally suppress things that Man, over the megayears, has learned the hard way—by evolution. Not all animals with big teeth are carnivores. Not all animals with claws are carnivores. Not all big animals are carnivores. But if you enter a region that is totally strange to you, and you see a large animal, with large pointed teeth, that has claws rather than hoofs, and does not have horns—you have no logical data, of course, about the nature of this individual, it's just pure suspicion, but you're rather apt to live longer if you suspect it of being a hunting carnivore.

On the other hand, as Couvier, the great Zoologist pointed out, the traditional Devil is obviously herbiverous; he has horns and hoofs.

MAY   1955

A MATTER OF DEGREE

There has been very little study of the relationships between individuals, and the group generated by the interactions of those individuals—either at the level of purely mechanical units such as relays in a computer, or human beings in a culture. The introduction of the great electronic computers, and of ever more complex systems, and systems-of-systems, has led to a beginning of the study of systems-as-such.

The most pressing aspect of systems-problems has been the obviously high-priority one of systems failures. If we have ten thousand individual units each having a fifty per cent reliability in a one-thousand-hour run, how long can we expect the system, as a whole, to operate before failure, assuming the ten thousand units are connected in series? Answer: About six minutes.

Systems don't behave in quite as simple a way, however, when we have multiple-series-parallel connections, with crossover switching for substitution or bridging around defective units, plus feedback for internal self-checking, plus dynamic homeostasis systems, and a few of the other simpler types of arrangements the systems engineers have introduced for improved reliability. The boys in the drafting rooms are beginning to consult the biologists, and the neurologists are starting to look up from computer journals with a sudden realization of the order of, "Sooooo—so *that's* why the third ganglion of . . . hm-m-m . . ." Living organisms have been evolving solutions—purely pragmatic, but extremely competent after three to four billion years of field testing—to systems reliability problems too, of course. Negative and positive feedback systems—telemetering—servomechanisms—amplifier systems—miniaturization to make a miniaturization engineer tear his hair—it's all been there for a billion years or so.

Most of the naturally evolved systems are so darned highly evolved that human engineering can't figure out what in blazes the thing's built that way for. Usually the miniaturization technique has been carried down to a sub-molecular level, which makes it just a bit difficult for the engineer to trace out the circuits, even if he knew what the circuits were doing.

On the other extreme, the humanic fields are stopped just as completely because the structures they are studying are equally complex, and so huge that a man's-eye-view makes it as difficult to see the shape of the whole system-of-systems involved in a culture, as it is for a man to see the shape of the Earth. The tools for expressing the problem, moreover, are the inherently inadequate tools developed before the existence of the problem was recognized—language that's based on linear logic. Modern languages and thinking-systems work like a chain of links, and are inherently unsuitable for expression of a system-of-systems that works like a rope. Our formal method of discussion denies the use of analogical thinking, and refuses to consider that ten concurrent items, each having a truth-and-relevancy probability of fifty per cent, can constitute high-probability evidence. After all, logically each one of them can be shown to be too untrustworthy for consideration.

The social scientists—and in that group I include psychologists, psychotherapists, sociologists, anthropologists, linguistics specialists, and historians—are struggling with tools inadequate to their task, and struggling with the fact that the new tools can't be invented so long as the Rules of Evidence remain unmodified.

Being a science-fiction editor, I can speculate; anyone interested is invited to speculate along with me, in the full realization that no formally acceptable evidence can be educed to establish the validity of the speculations. This is reasoning by analogy, which every one knows is of no value in a truly logical discussion.

I suggest that in two populations, having a normal distribution of characteristic Alpha, such that population A has the peak of the distribution curve as little as 0.1% off the peak of that characteristic for population B, may, *as a system*, differ in *kind*, not merely in degree. That Population A, in other words, may by its interactions, produce a system of type X, while population B, in its interactions, solely because of that 0.1% difference, may produce a different *kind* of system, type Y.

If this proposition can be validated, that would imply that very minor shifts in the peak of a distribution curve could produce huge differences in the nature of the resultant culture.

The speculation is based on the following analogical reasoning: a human population, in its interactions, is a very complex system of information relay units. The "grapevine" communication system is a tremendously powerful force in shaping the reaction of any population—and grapevine communication involves multiple-parallel information relaying, with an almost indescribably complex system of feedbacks, cross-checkings, shunts, filtering systems, distorting forces, damping forces, and what not. An individual unit in the interacting complex may have a personal bias that causes him to block passage of information of type 1, while strongly amplifying and reinforcing information of type 2. For information of type 1 he acts as a damping filter; for type 2 he's a resonant amplifier.

Due to his interconnections, with type 2 information, he'll excite (transmit to) twenty contacts, and reinforce the input information strongly in transmitting it. Perhaps for type 3, or type 17 information, he's an inverter-amplifier—he actively denies and suppresses any such information. He will spend time and effort seeking out individuals who have the information, and seeking to destroy their belief in its validity. Other individuals may organize to establish blocks in the system seeking to make the entire system non-conductive for information of a specific type. In our current culture, information on sex and various other subjects is actively blocked by organized groups, for example.

All in all, the complex interactions of human individuals in a culture constitutes an enormously complex information filtering and relaying system, with both positive and negative feedback at all stages, complex shunts around blocks, and altogether constituting an unanalyzably involved system.

However some of the general characteristics of such very complex systems have been solved in a quite different area—in the field of nucleonics!

A standard nuclear reactor represents a complex population of different components, having different characteristics with respect to two critical phenomena; neutrons and fission reactions.

Present in a nuclear reactor there will be U-235, U-238, a moderator such as graphite or heavy water, and various impurities, plus control rods, which are simply controllable impurities having neutron-absorbing characteristics.

If a neutron reaches a U-235 nucleus, it normally causes fission; the U-235 nucleus can, for our purposes, be considered a neutron-amplifier, since it gives off 2-plus neutrons for each neutron absorbed. All the other substances present are neutron-absorbers, tending to damp out the neutron-signals released by the U-235 neutron-amplifiers. Some neutrons will be lost by escape through the boundaries of the reactor.

If the net gain due to the U-235 "neutron amplifiers" is exactly equal to the total loss of neutrons to all other components, the intensity of the nuclear reaction will be constant at whatever level it happens to be. The overall situation is, under this condition, that, on the average, the birth rate of neutrons in the system equals exactly the death rate, so that the neutron population is constant. The net neutron reproduction constant is, then, 1.000000. This neutron reproduction rate is referred to as the k-factor of the reactor.

However, if the k-factor is 1.0000001, each succeeding generation of neutrons is slightly more numerous; the neutron population is rising, and the level of activity of the reactor going up. In a reactor, the time per generation of neutrons is exceedingly short; the rate of rise of activity will be decidedly noticeable, even with so minute an excess over 1.000. . . .

On the inverse side, if k = 0.9999999 . . . , the rate of reaction is falling, the system is being damped, and will eventually settle down to zero reaction.

In such a system then, if k departs from exactly 1.000 . . . by even a minute degree, the system, as a whole, heads either for zero, or infinity. In the atomic bomb, we have a nuclear reactor with a high k factor, and the system heads for an infinite rate of reaction at a spectacularly high rate. Yet the bomb is perfectly safe and stable until triggered, because the system has been so designed that, until triggered, the k factor is held below 1.0000, and the reaction rate is, therefore, practically zero.

Now herein lies the peculiarity of this type of system-reaction;

a minute difference in degree—the k-factor—produces, because of the chain interaction system, *a difference of kind.* If k is less than 1.0000, the reactor *does not* react; if k exceeds 1.0000, the reactor *does* react. A tiny difference of degree becomes, in a complexly interacting system of this type, an Aristotelian difference of Yes or No.

In a nuclear reactor, the k-factor is controlled usually by inserting or withdrawing the neutron-absorbing material of the control rods. The reactor system, as a whole, is highly sensitive to very small changes in the amount of neutron-absorbing material present; a little too much neutron-absorption, and the nuclear reaction damps out completely. A little too little . . . and things get frantic rather suddenly; the safety rods drive home, alarm bells sound off, various automatic damping devices shut down everything, and start yelling for somebody to find out what in blazes went wrong.

But any human culture is a complexly interacting group. There are individuals who will amplify and transmit certain classes of information—and others who damp it out.

Who wants to bet that a very slight shift in the peak of the population's distribution curve can't make the whole system suddenly become highly reactive to a type of idea that, theretofore, it was totally unreactive to?

Just a few less idea-dampers, or a few more idea-amplifiers—and the system may "go critical" with respect to that idea.

Sure—it's just a matter of degree, not of kind, at the level of individual characteristics.

But it's a matter of *kind* at the level of system response!

October   1957

ON THE SELECTIVE BREEDING
OF HUMAN BEINGS

The current estimates of astrophysicists indicate that our local galaxy is something like 300,000 light-years in circumference. The solar system is moving through space—in a great orbit about the galactic center—at about a dozen miles a second. Now obviously that sort of snail-pace crawl is never going to get us anywhere in transgalactic, or circumgalactic travel.

Well . . . it won't in one man's lifetime—or even in the lifetime of Herr Hitler's boasted 1,000-year Reich. (Even if it had come off!)

However, astrophysicists also estimate that the Solar System is now on about its twenty-fifth swing around the galactic center. After all, five billion years isn't anything too overwhelming to a normal, main-sequence star, nicely stabilized in the G-range of spectrum types. Just because 200,000,000 years seems rather long to us—well, there are different time-scales to apply to different phenomena. Present theories suggest our Sun should be good for another two hundred fifty swings around the galaxy before reaching old age.

What is, and is-not possible or practicable many times depends on the time-scale imposed; a dozen miles a second is an "impossible" speed for circumnavigating the entire galaxy, is it?

I've had a good many arguments on the subject of selective breeding of human beings—not on the subject of whether or not it should be done, or is ethical, but on whether or not it can be done at all. The essential argument against the possibility is in essence: "You can't eliminate recessive characteristics! They'll hide in the germ-plasm where you can't tell they're there, and crop out again one thousand—two thousand—five thousand years later. You'll never be able to get rid of a characteristic you've decided against! No human plan has ever lasted even one thousand years, let alone five thousand!"

In other words, the argument is that the rate of advance is impossibly slow with respect to the distance to be covered. And that simply suggests that the wrong time scale is being considered.

I'd like to suggest to the attention of geneticists and animal breeders in general, some consideration of the problem of selective breeding of human beings—with a time scale of the order appropriate to evolutionary phenomena. Say let's consider what can be done in 50 kiloyears or so, by the application of extremely harsh culling of the rejected types.

Properly, we should talk in terms of kilogenerations rather than kiloyears; after all, it's the number of generations that counts— not the time-span involved. Modern human racial types tend toward a twenty-five-year generation, but the most primitive human types still surviving tend toward a ten- to fifteen-year generation; the females start producing young at eleven to twelve years of age, and average something approaching one per year for another twelve years or so. (Most of the young die, of course, in infancy—but the rate of production is high.) In the earliest protohuman groups, we can assume a generation was shorter, and some ten generations could be packed into a century.

Anthropologists seem to feel that human tribes have existed for a minimum of 250,000 years; we can say that's a minimum of ten thousand generations, and probably somewhat nearer eight thousand generations.

Now recessive characteristics that don't manifest themselves in a span of one thousand generations must be really quite recessive —recessive enough that we can be quite unperturbed by their phenomenally rare appearance. Albinos exist, and varicolored skin appears occasionally—a sort of "pinto" human being—but we don't have to disturb ourselves greatly about those unimportant rarities.

Then any selective breeding system that could maintain a program of selection for a period of one thousand *generations*, not one thousand years, would have some real effect. Moreover, if the selective mechanism were utterly ruthless, savagely harsh, and culled so hard and tight as to destroy sixty per cent of the young produced each generation—a level of ruthless selectivity no modern human group would countenance for a moment!—considerable effect could be produced in selective breeding of human beings.

I propose to show that precisely such a selective breeding system did in fact—and still does—operate. I want, first, to make it absolutely clear that I am NOT making any moral-ethical judgments whatever. It is a fact that wolves produce a selective breeding effect on deer herds; this is readily observed, without any need for moral judgment as to whether they should or should not do so.

In the same purely observational sense, I want to show that human beings have been selectively bred by a mechanism that does have the requisite long time-span effect to make one thousand years like a day in its sight—one thousand years or one thousand generations.

There are two things that set Man apart from the animals. (Observable things, that is! The question of *soul* we'll have to skip because we can't observe it.) One: Man has the ability to use symbolic abstractions. (A certain few animals have this ability to some slight degree.) Two: Man has the ability to override his instinctive behavior patterns by intellectual-training ideas. No other animal has that ability.

Please note: that ability is not absolute in Man, nor is it even yet invariably present in all men. There are indications that baboons have some degree of symbolization language, and strong indications that porpoises also have a language. Let's consider the problem of the very early proto-human proto-tribe; in essence, it was to distinguish the Men from the Monkeys, among the progeny produced.

One thing that helps on making the thing possible is that the human race has a nearly-unique situation; the human male can rape the female without her consent or co-operation—something impossible to practically all other mammalian species. This is somewhat more important than it at first appears. If the males of the proto-tribe are going to select the young produced, and destroy the ones they consider unacceptable—the female's instincts are to protect her young, and to find and mate with males who will accept and protect her young. The proto-human females would have refused to mate with males who destroyed their young, if they were able to refuse! There's no use having a good, valid idea . . . if you can't make it work, you know. If the females had been able to block it, it wouldn't have worked.

So Item #1 in the proto-human males: They could overcome the ancient mammalian instinct to accept and protect *all* their female's progeny.

Obviously the No. 1 test for Man vs. Monkey was whether the individual young learned to use language. All indications available suggest that those who didn't pass the test were converted to food for the tribe; cannibalism was, at the period under discussion, *de rigueur*.

That individuals incapable of learning to use language were flunked from the proto-tribe is fairly understandable; a group having a really rugged struggle to achieve a subsistence level of existence doesn't support incompetents. It can't. It has a better use for them—as food.

Please try to get something of the viewpoint of these proto-humans. They were not human . . . yet. They were not sentimental; they were, equally, not cruel. A falling tree may crush a child, and hold it pinned helpless, while it dies slowly in screaming agony; still, the tree is not cruel. A wolf kills a fawn; it is not cruel, either—simply hungry. The early proto-humans were incapable of cruelty; that is an attitude, a concept, beyond the reach of their very unsubtle minds. Cruelty requires sophistication; these proto-humans utterly lacked it.

If they caught four members of an alien tribe, only one of whom could be eaten by the tribe that day, they broke the arms and legs of the other three. This kept the extra supply of meat fresh and unspoiled until it, too, could be eaten while very simply and directly preventing escape. This was not cruelty; it was lack of refrigeration.

The young who did not learn to use speech were recognized as nonmen, as animals, and eaten.

Maintain that system for some one to ten kilogenerations . . . and it's a very, very effective selective breeding system. Even recessive nonspeech genes will get combed out.

Oh, of course they ate a few who couldn't learn to speak because of hearing defects, or vocal anomalies, who were, otherwise, perfectly sound carriers of sound genes. But that was quite unimportant; the females were always producing more young than could be fed anyway. And the hearing defect might have been a genetic anomaly too . . . so into the pot with him.

Note that once a proto-human proto-tribe capable of speech arises, it will inevitably become a self-perpetuating selective-breeding system that culls out all nonspeaking young produced. And this tendency won't continue just for a few generations—just while a particular dynasty of tribal leaders prevails. It has a characteristic that will make it continue as a basic of the tribe *so long as the tribe exists.*

Since tribes capable of speech have a very, very real advantage over nonspeaking herds, the tribe will persist indefinitely.

If it is overcome and destroyed—it's almost certain that only another speaking tribe will be able to organize sufficiently to defeat it.

And, incidentally, note that War was invented by proto-humans as a necessary, racial-benefiting system. Any speaking tribe has so great an advantage over any nonspeaking herd that with only animal enemies, wild and destructive variants could rise to lethal concentration before being eliminated. A speaking tribe could go off on some intrinsically destructive aberrant development and go beyond the point of no return if only animal predators menaced it. But with alien speaking tribes around to menace—they will be forced to fly right, or get clipped quick.

Only other men, that is, constituted adequate judges of human or proto-human tribes.

Given a few thousand generations—and tribal life has been going on for at least ten thousand generations—the selective breeding system produced a pure-bred strain of speech-gifted people. Today, even our lowest idiots, defective as they are, maintain that very, very, deeply inbred ability. Nonspeaking genes were, in the proto-tribal environment, absolutely lethal genes, having a one hundred per cent infant mortality effect. Even recessive nonspeaking genes get pretty thoroughly eliminated in the course of ten thousand generations.

Sure it's hard to breed out recessive characteristics—and at twelve miles a second it takes a long time to get around the galaxy. That doesn't mean it's impossible; it just means it takes time. A quarter million years of time, for eliminating nonspeaking Monkeys from the race of Men.

Now obviously the time to eliminate carriers of defective genes is *before* they breed, not afterward. That is, the young should be tested for defects before being allowed to mate; passing the tests would then give the testee the right to take a mate and start breeding. They would, in other words, be the Manhood Rites.

Any anthropologist can assure you that Manhood Rites are universally found among tribes on all the continents all over the planet. Since the African Negroes, the South American Indians and the Australian Aborigines have had no cultural common origin in the last thirty thousand years, it's fair indication that the Manhood Rites ceremonies have been effectively part of the human tribal system for at least thirty thousand years. That alone would be quite an extensive selective breeding force.

Now there is one basic feature that is common to practically all Manhood Rites ceremonies everywhere; trial by ordeal.

Remember that one of the two crucial tests that separates Man from Monkey is that a Man can, by rational intellectual effort overcome, override, his instinctive controls. He can do what his instincts violently forbid, and can refrain from doing what his instincts command. A Monkey cannot.

You can train an animal to jump through a flaming hoop—by teaching him the fact that the fire does not hurt. You can not teach an animal to hold still while a burning brand is thrust against its flesh to sear the flesh—to hold still, while the stink of its own burning meat rises into its nostrils. You can teach an animal that its instinctive response *does not apply in this case;* it can then jump through the burning hoop. But the instinct *does* apply when a red-hot coal is burning its way into its flesh.

Three extremely powerful instinctive pain-dread systems exist in animals: 1. Thou shalt not allow thy protective skin to be penetrated lest thou die!

2. Thou shalt not allow thy teeth to be destroyed, for without them, thou cannot nourish thyself!

3. Thou shalt protect thy genitals with thy life, for without them thou shalt die genetically.

In other words, skin, teeth, and genitals all have very high instinctive survival value.

Typical Manhood Rites involve ordeals by fire, involving *real*, not mock, destructive burning of the skin, or cutting the skin of the chest in two places, forcing a leather strap through from one slit to the other, and requiring that the boy tear the strap out through his skin, and scarifying tattooing-the-hard-way. Tooth-filing is another quite standard Manhood test. And circumcision is one of the oldest and most widespread. (The Jews moved it from Manhood to babyhood—but by then, they'd developed some quite different and more important tests.)

I think it will be unequivocally agreed that no Monkey could pass any one of these tests—for the real essence of it is that *verbal commands alone must suffice to override ancient, and valid instincts!*

Because they are *valid* instincts. Occasionally, individuals are born without a sense of pain; such individuals could, of course, pass the ordeal test without any difficulty whatever . . . if they could just manage to live that long. The pain instincts are valid; you can't live without them. The essence of the ancient tribal tests is that a Man, unlike a Monkey, can, by intellectual-volition override valid instincts, in real, not mock, situations.

When the Manhood Rites ordeals started, it's a fair bet that every boy who lost the battle to control his instincts, and ran from the searing brand on his flesh, contributed to the celebration banquet of the successful Men. Not because the tribesmen were cruel, nor because they were punishing him for running— but because he had turned out to be a Monkey, not a Man, and roast Monkey was a standard item of diet anyway.

The tribe that relaxed its tests—that stopped culling the Monkeys from their Men—was aberrant, a defective tribe, and was presently destroyed by some neighboring tribe. Because Monkeys will not face real, personal pain in battle, simply because they must protect their fellow-tribesmen. A Monkey will not take high risk of pain and death—will not, because he cannot override the automatic instinct pilot-controls—just to save fellow tribesmen.

We, today, benefit from the ancient Manhood Rites selective breeding system that went on for tens of thousands of generations, whenever a jet pilot, in a plane with a flamed-out engine, rides his flying coffin into the ground . . . so it won't fall into a school-yard, a hospital, or a suburban development. He does it because his ancestors were Men, not Monkeys—they passed the test of Manhood. They earned the right to breed.

Our ancestors may have been ignorant in many things—but they were not stupid, nor were they fools. They found ways to selectively breed Men from Monkeys—and they had the cold, high, and ruthless determination to do it.

Man has been defined as a "rational animal"; the ancient animal instincts are essential to being a Man. The ancient pain instinct, the ancient instinct to find a mate and breed—without these the individual and his line would die. Yet the essence of the "rational" part of the definition is that Man can override the instinct controls for cause.

An individual specimen with that strange characteristic must arise constantly among the Monkeys; the difference is that ten thousand generations of selective breeding have produced, in Man, a genetic norm that has that characteristic.

But that is a far more subtle and complex question than the simple "speaks" or "can't speak"; the ability to speak has been almost absolutely stabilized in Man. The ability to override instinct for rational cause cannot be so sharply and simply defined at any level higher than the level of physical pain.

The modern rapist, who cannot override an instinctive drive, would present a very simple problem to our ancestors. "He is not a Man, but a Monkey; destroy him."

The more subtle levels of rational overcontrol are still in process of selection; never, in all time to come, will the necessity for selective breeding of human beings end, however. There are not only outcroppings of recessive genes to fight—there are always negative mutations that regenerate the eliminated and rejected genes. There will be Monkeys who cannot learn speech born, through all future ages. There are, and will be, Monkeys who cannot take rational command from the automatic-pilot of instincts born. Through all the ages ahead, both types, when born, must be denied membership in the race of Man.

Currently, there's another level of selective breeding needed —and coming up. The Tribal Man was selectively bred for the characteristic that training and instruction should be able to override instinct.

What we know as Civilization requires a higher characteristic; that judgment of an immediate, present instance be able to override *both training and instinct*.

The Monkey was required to give up his reliance on instinct to become a Man; the Tribesman must give up his reliance on instinct *and training* to become a Citizen.

The Monkey's sense of rightness-and-security was, basically, derived from all his ancestors—instinctive. The Tribesman derived his sense of rightness and security from all his tribe—the training in ritual and taboo. The Citizen must derive his sense of rightness from his own judgments—without losing sight of the fact that his judgments can be wrong.

The Citizen, poor guy, has to get along without any sense of security; it is a luxury he can't afford, if he is to live by judgment, instead of Traditional Training or Instinct.

FEBRUARY   1961

ASTROLOGER—ASTRONOMER—
ASTRO-ENGINEER

Some of the greatest minds in the history of human science are Copernicus, Tycho Brahe, Johannes Kepler, Galileo, and Isaac Newton.

These men did certain work, concerning certain observational data, for certain motivations. They were five great Astrologers.

Running an article on the nature and development of astrology in this magazine—or any other magazine directed primarily to a technically oriented readership—calls for some explanation. It has been thoroughly, solidly, completely established, for a couple of centuries now, that astrology is superstitious nonsense.

Since that solid decision is now a couple of centuries old, and is flatly in contradiction of five of the keenest minds the human race is known to have produced, it is at least reasonable to review the decision at this point and see if modern data does, in fact, confirm the now centuries-old conclusions. (Be it remembered that, in essence, an "old superstition" is a conclusion reached by people several centuries previously, without adequate grounds, and which has not been rationally reviewed since. In that sense, the proposition "Astrology is superstitious nonsense" is itself a superstition!)

The two areas of research that most fascinated Isaac Newton were astrology and alchemy. Through a long period of the Renaissance the most able technically inclined minds of Mankind were engaged in studies of astrology and alchemy.

Alchemy—in the sense of the search for the Philosopher's Stone, and the transmutation of base metals to gold—proved a complete bust. Transmutation we now know is perfectly possible . . . but not by any chemical manipulation. The Philosopher's Stone was a completely false goal.

Astrology broke down into something considered quite different—Astronomy. We now say that Tycho Brahe was a great *as-*

tronomer, and that those other great men were also early *astronomers*.

Were they? They didn't say so! To decide the question, we must, first, get some sort of a definition of the difference between "astrology" and "astronomy." You think you can do that easily? Oh . . . "Astrology is that superstitious nonsense about predicting future events on Earth by studying the positions of the stars and planets."

And how do the United States government agencies set about predicting the tides? By astrology—if that's the definition of Astrology.

Oh . . . that's different, because that's simple gravitational force computation? You mean, then, "it ain't what you do, it's the way that you do it!"

Then Kepler couldn't help being an astrologer. Since gravity hadn't been defined at the time he was doing his work, when he computed tides by studying the aspects of the Sun and Moon, he was an astrologer. A later computer predicting tides by studying the aspects of the Sun and Moon, however, would not be an astrologer, even though he did exactly the same things, because he knew that gravity existed. That it?

Hm-m-m . . . and what *is* this "gravity"? Is it anything like *"elan vital"* or *phlogiston?* They explained observed phenomena also, though, at the time, they could not themselves be defined.

No, somehow that doesn't satisfy. The modern computer uses Kepler's laws, and the laws of that later, greater astrologer, Newton, and essentially not only does *what* Kepler did, but does it the *way* Kepler did.

It seems to me the real difference is purely subjective—which is why the oh-so-strictly-objective scientist doesn't care to try to define the difference. The difference is purely a matter of motivation—not of action nor of process. If Q. Publicus killed B. Marcus by running him through with his short sword, was Q. Publicus a murderer? No, Q. Publicus was the executioner designated by his Centurion to dispose of B. Marcus, traitor. Murder is determined not by action nor by method, but by motive.

And even that differentiation can get a bit subtle at times. Most alchemists got into the business partly from pure curiosity

—basic research—and considerably for reasons of making money. The modern chemist gets into the business partly through the urge of pure curiosity, and partly to make a living. And the nuclear physicist is trying to perfect his transmutation techniques just as his ancestral alchemist was!

The error in alchemy was that they were trying to do a level of work that could not be handled until several centuries of additional, lower-level data had been accumulated. They were trying to enter the era of nucleonics before they'd learned what the elements were.

There were some three centuries of chemical engineering between where they were and where they thought they were—at the border of the nuclear era.

The astrologers were in somewhat the same position; they needed a very great deal more information about such fundamentals as celestial mechanics, nuclear physics, radiation physics, high-energy particle emission, ionic phenomena, magnetic field effects . . . oh, a very great deal!—before they could even begin to get some of what they thought they were ready for. And, of course, they had a lot of false ideas of what they could get anyway—just as the alchemists thought they could get the Philosopher's Stone.

Basically, Astrology started several millennia ago, when early men first observed the immense effect the cycles of the stars had on events here on Earth. The early Egyptians and Babylonians had no slightest conception of *why* the world grew colder when the cycle of the stars brought Orion rising in the east at twilight —or *why* the world grew warmer again when Lyra rose at dusk, and Orion was no longer visible.

Earliest civilized man observed a very simple, direct, and absolutely unchallengeable fact-of-nature. The movements of the stars predicted the changing of the climate with perfect reliability.

They had not the slightest notion why. But then, they didn't know *why* planting a seed caused a plant to come up. When the world is one vast collection of mysteries, the business of a wise man is to establish some sound, reliable correlations, letting the questions of *why* go until he has more information.

At that stage of history, Man was acutely aware that he had to learn how to make sense out of the Universe he found around him—not demand that the Universe make sense in his terms if it wanted him to accept it!

To us it is obvious that the perfect one-to-one correlation between the cycles of the stars and the climate on Earth was *not* an observation of a cause-effect relationship, but of two effects of a single cause. The clock may mark the time of sunrise, but that correlation doesn't prove the clock causes the sun to rise. Obvious . . . to us.

By the time man's first fairly complex high-level civilizations had built themselves, over many laborious centuries, the knowledge that the movements of the stars accurately predicted events on Earth was one of the unarguable established facts. As solidly proven as the fact that planting seeds was necessary to get a crop.

However . . . planting seeds, while necessary, is unfortunately not sufficient to assure a crop. Planting seeds is a Strong and Necessary Magic, and undeniably a very sound and Powerful Magic for crop-producing. (And it's *magic*, bub . . . when you haven't, by several thousand years, reached the stage of building microscopes and ultracentrifuges and microchemical analytical systems capable of studying the immense complexities of RNA and DNA and cytoplasm and genetics.) Just because a Magic doesn't work every time does not—very definitely not!—mean you should reject it as nonsense. Is there anything more supernaturally improbable than that this dry, withered, seemingly dead bit of woody stuff should turn itself somehow into an immense tree? Why, no tale of magical transformation out of the Arabian Nights ever surpassed that!

So . . . given the factual knowledge that the predictable cycles of the stars foretold the coming of events on Earth, it remained only to achieve more sophisticated methods of interpreting the patterns of star-movements to determine the finer details of events on Earth.

Now perhaps we can define an Astrologer as one who studies the stars to establish his conviction that human events on Earth can be predicted by the movements of the stars, and to perfect his ability thereby to predict human events more acutely.

An Astronomer studies the stars to determine what and where they are . . . because he wants to understand the stars.

As of the beginning of the Space Age, we can specify a third profession—the Astro-engineer, who studies the stars *in order to predict what effects they are going to have on human engineering projects.*

An engineer studying the possibilities of a tidal power project would be one example of astro-engineering.

Now be it noted that Alchemy has been dead and dishonored for a couple of centuries, and all sound, properly educated Scientists knew that Transmutation was Impossible, by 1880. Chemistry had, by then rejected *in toto* the concepts of alchemy—philosopher's stone, Earth, Air, Fire and Water, transmutation of the elements—the works.

So here we are transmuting elements, and aware that transmutation of the elements is *the* basic process that makes the Universe go round.

But here we are also being so amazingly astute and wise that we know for a positive fact that the positions of the planets has nothing whatever to do with any events here on Earth. Oh, the Moon, yes, of course! But what effect could Jupiter, or Saturn, or Mars have on human affairs? How could they possibly affect anything here on Earth? What nonsense to suggest that the relative positions of planets could have any meaning!

And then we have the work of John Nelson, Communications Engineer, who I suggest might well be classified as an Astroengineer, who has learned to study the positions of the planets in order to predict their effects on human engineering problems.

That solar flares disrupted radio communications here on Earth was a readily ascertained fact—as soon as we had radio communications to be disrupted. Magnetic storms caused by solar flares had been raising hob with maritime navigation for centuries; a ship's compass points generally northward, unless there's a magnetic storm, in which case it's just as apt to point East, West, or if it has a chance, Straight Up. As long power lines were strung across the country, and telegraph and telephone lines, we learned a new aspect of the storms—they could induce perfectly deadly voltages and currents in long conductors.

John Nelson has shown—by making ninety-three per cent accurate predictions, when a time accuracy of ±10 minutes at 5-day ranges—that the occurrence of solar flares can be predicted by observing the patterns of the planets.

Now this is something entirely new in observational science; it is a proven instance of a *pattern* having an effect that the *elements of the pattern* do not have. It's true that chemists ran into that phenomenon at the molecular level—CH_3-O-CH_3 has the same elements as CH_3 CH_2 OH but a radically different effect! —but to find that a *pattern-arrangement of the planets* has immensely significant effects that the planets themselves do not is a very different thing indeed.

And it means that a phenomenon has been demonstrated to be valid without anyone yet having been able to explain why it is valid. It works . . . and we don't know why.

I fear that, little as Science likes that situation, that is a problem that will arise through all the megayears of history yet to come. Obviously any time a really new phenomenon is stumbled on, it will have exactly that characteristic.

Nelson's work during the past seven years has been of immense value to the communications industry; his motivation in studying the stars and planets is not that of the astrologer, nor that of the astronomer. He's not interested in the stars and planets for their own sakes; he's interested in them as what I think we should call an astro-engineer—to find out how to arrange his engineering problem, long distance communications by radio, in view of the observed effects those bodies have.

When a solar flare lets loose, it would be quite appropriate to say that all Hell is out for noon. The article "Gravity Insufficient," by Hal Clement, in the November 1961 issue gave a discussion of what has been found out about solar flares and their effects. It's painfully clear that when a solar flare cuts loose, any man outside of Earth's atmosphere—and no man has yet gone outside; neither Russian nor American capsules were beyond the protective layers of the upper atmosphere—in any space-capsule present technology can lift off the ground would be a well cooked goose. If he were in an orbit at 100,000 miles—he'd have to be about that far out to get beyond the normal Van Allen belt—he'd have to spend days getting there, making one orbit, and getting back. If a flare occurred at any time during that period, he would be completely helpless.

A flare can develop in a period of about fifteen minutes. Eight minutes after it gets going, the X-radiation arrives at Earth's orbit, X-radiation of a hardness and intensity such that any shielding we could lift off the launching pad would be useless.

If the astro- or cosmo-naut caught out in the solar storm started for home right then . . . it would be futile. Remember, the limitations of modern technology will mean he has to come in by using retrorockets to change his near-circular orbit to a grazing-ellipse orbit. And to get through the *normal* Van Allen belt safely, he must break his orbit at the right part of its 320,000 mile circumference and come in to the lower atmosphere through one of the magnetic-polar tunnels through the Van Allen radiations. He won't have rocket power enough to simply turn his ship around, blast for home on an emergency short-cut orbit, and get out of the solar storm.

It would take him a day or more on the fastest orbit home he could make.

Beginning a few minutes after the X rays arrive at the speed of light, some extremely high-speed electrons will be showing up. They won't penetrate even the thin metal walls of a space-capsule . . . but the X rays generated when the walls do stop them will. Shortly after the fastest electrons will come the fastest nuclei—protons largely, traveling at very near light-speed. Gradually, the intensity of radiation will increase as the greater numbers of slower protons and electrons make the 93,000,000 mile trip from the Sun.

Long before the spaceman could get down even so far as the outer Van Allen belt, that belt would be enormously surcharged with trapped ions from the solar flare. The radiation in the belts would, by that time, be so deadly as to kill him in minutes if he did try penetrating.

Any astronaut caught off Earth in a modern space-capsule—or any in the foreseeable future of present technology—will be as dead as if he'd taken a swim on one of those swimming-pool reactors.

The space agencies of all nations will have to employ astro-engineers like John Nelson, who can predict what's going to happen to human engineering projects, by studying the pattern of positions of the planets.

One can imagine the shop-talk of a couple of astrogators in years ahead. "Well, on this run we had to get through before May 31st, or the line lost that contract for good. But look, we had Jupiter and Saturn practically dead-on at quadrature, with Mars in opposition to Saturn. Earth was neutral, and the only favorable planet we had was Venus in trine with Jupiter. So Harmonson, the damn fool, says sure we can make it, and accepts the run! With a planetary pattern like that he thinks he can get by without a flare, yet! So . . ."

They'll sound like astrologers. They certainly won't sound like astronomers—because astrogators won't be interested in the stars and planets for their own sweet sakes. They'll be very strictly practical in their interests; they won't care *why* certain planetary patterns trigger solar flares—but they'll have an acute personal interest in the fact *that* they do! They'll carefully consult the pattern of the planets to determine whether their aspects are propitious. If they've got Jupiter, Saturn and Mars situated 120° apart around the Sun, it'll be a milk run. The Sun doesn't flare, when those planets are 120° apart.

It was the alchemists, not chemists, who first learned to make oil of vitriol, and corrosive sublimate and aqua regia—and our modern technological culture would break down without the megatons of oil of vitriol we need.

It begins to look, now, as though it's time to go back and glean through astrology, with the vast funds of new knowledge and new techniques available.

We're damn well going to need astro-engineers in the next few decades!

HYDROGEN ISN'T CULTURAL

In the February 1957 issue of Astounding Science Fiction, H. Beam Piper had a story "Omnilingual" concerning the translation of the Martian language, found in the 50,000-plus year-old ruins. The anthropologists and linguists insisted that, since there could be no Rosetta Stone bilingual key, relating the unknown Martian writings to a known language, no translation would be possible.

Piper had a very simple, but enormously powerful point to make; the Martians had had a highly developed technology of chemistry, electricity, mechanics, et cetera. And chemistry is not a matter of cultural opinion; it's a matter of the "opinion" of the Universe. It makes not the slightest difference whether you're a Martian, a Russian, an American, or an inhabitant of the fourth planet of a KO star in the Lesser Magellanic Cloud; hydrogen behaves in one, and only one way. Because the term "hydrogen" is a human-language symbol for a specific set of behavior characteristics, and, in this universe, that set of behavior characteristics requires the interaction of a single proton and a single electron in an atomic structure. (There may be 0, 1, or 2 neutrons with only minute variations of the chemical properties, though the resultant nuclear characteristics are widely different.)

Any highly developed technology of chemistry will have a term referring to that pattern-of-characteristics; it *has* to have. The pattern of characteristics is a function not of the culture, but of the Universe itself. Whether you call a certain element "sauerstoff" or "oxygen" makes no difference; the behavior characteristics of the hydride of that element will remain the same.

Technically, under international agreement, there is no such element as "tungsten" any more—but the metal they use for incandescent lamp filaments maintains the same characteristic of phenomenally high melting point, whether it be called "tungsten" or "wolfram." No alien-star culture can develop a chemical system in which that element dissolves in dilute sulfuric acid and melts at 1100°C.; the laws of the Universe, not the agreements of intelligent entities is involved.

Perhaps the scientists working on the problem of cracking the genetic code should take time out to read H. Beam Piper's story. It might help in understanding one of the "mysteries of the genetic code" that has been discovered recently.

The communication system of genetics appears to be based on information encoded in the very complex arrangement of amino acid units in the giant molecules of deoxyribonucleic acid—DNA. A great deal of work has been done on some of the simpler, and more tractable organisms—microorganisms usually, because they're cheap, reproduce rapidly, and are "the small economy size."

The colon bacillus has been a favorite; it's hardy, handy, and prolific and—which is *not* an unimportant consideration!—it's not a dangerously lethal organism.

Certain "codons," or groupings of three-bases-together, are "words" in the "language" of genetics. There are four important amino-acid-bases; adenine, cystine, guanine and uracil. It is combinations of these four, taken three-at-a-time that make up the "words," or *codons.*

The codons are genetic-language "words" which specify a particular amino acid which is to be incorporated in a protein molecule being constructed—an enzyme, hormone, or tissue component.

Careful research established that, in the genetic language of the colon bacillus, certain identified codons "meant" certain specific and identified amino acids. I.e., the biochemists had succeeded in translating some of the codons of the colon bacillus genetic language into human language.

A scientist of Polaris B IIc studying human chemistry might learn to translate the symbols HCl into his native symbols *~>; so human biochemists learned to translate *b. coli* genetic language into human language.

Our article "Cracking the Code," by Carl A. Larson, in the December, 1963 issue covers a good bit of the work done in that area. It's one of the neatest pieces of cross-collaboration between scientists in history; biologists, chemists, information-theory specialists, and computermen had to work as a team to get the answers.

Recently, scientists in that field have been able to make another important experimental step. If a specific codon, ACG, in *b. coli* geneticese "means" alanine—what does the codon ACG mean in the genetic language of other organisms? Or do all organisms "speak" the same genetic language?

The experiments performed recently by Dr. I. Bernard Weinstein, of the Columbia University College of Physicians and Surgeons, strongly indicate that *all terrestrial organisms "speak" the same genetic language.*

The identification of meaning of colon bacillus codons permitted checking those specific codons in the genetic DNA of other organisms, and determining whether these other organisms used the same "dictionary" of codons. Six specific codons were checked for "meaning" in the genetic language of a protozoon, *Chalmydomonas,* rat liver cells, and mouse tumor cells. All six codons, in each type of cell, correlated with the same specific amino acids.

The language for all these widely different organisms was the same, at least with respect to these six specific amino acids.

The evolutionary gap between *bacillus coli,* which belongs in the plant kingdom, and at an extremely primitive level, the protozoon, and the highly evolved rodent tissue cells is enormous. The branch-off of the plant and animal kingdoms must have occurred at least two billion years ago; the evolutionary level of the placental mammals represents perhaps a billion years of advance and development beyond the protozoon.

Any system of message encodement, that remains unchanged through some two thousand million years of transmission—through perhaps two *trillion* relayings from one generation to the next—has a most remarkable degree of stability. The encoding system carries genetic information; the genetic information is, of course, subject to mutation. It's those mutations over the megayears, that separated the bacillus, the protozoon and the rodents. But the *system of encoding* is evidently either absolutely immune to mutation, or so nearly so that not even two billion years of time, and two trillion relayings has altered it.

It's been suggested that the organisms all have the same genetic code because they all descended from the same original life-cell, and have not changed the coding since.

There's another possibility, however.

Nearly ten years ago, on a visit up to Cambridge, Massachusetts, I got together with a group of Harvard and MIT researchers —all science-fiction readers—in a fine bull-session discussion.

With "malice aforethought," I threw in for discussion the following problem: Suppose that for some reason it is necessary to deposit a message on a planet—we'll make it a planet like the Earth—which is to be recoverable after a period of two billion years.

Now carving it in a mountainside won't work for that period of time. Nor will engraving it on platinum-iridium plates, even if we deposit hundreds of engraved plates all over the surface of the planet.

We'll make the message something relatively simple and specific, so we can discuss it—we'll say it's a statement concerning the interaction of carbon dioxide and water.

The discussion took off in fine fashion—and it was really being analyzed by some *highly* competent minds. As I recall, Claude Shannon, the founder of Information Theory, was there, and Warren Seaman, of the Harvard Computer Labs, Wayne Batteau, Instrumentation Theory specialist, and some of the men working on the machine translation of language at the Harvard Computer Labs.

It was strictly a discussion of a problem for the fun of analyzing problems; it lasted well over an hour and a half before they'd agreed on a general technique that could preserve such a message, on such a planet, over such a period of time.

To begin with, trying to establish some monument that can be stable against all tectonic, chemical and erosive attacks for any such period of time is nonsense; give up. A method of multiple-record must be used; the message must be inscribed so many times that even if a million copies are lost, there will be plenty more to be recovered.

But the use of multiple-record introduces problems of error-multiplication. Moreover, no number of copies distributed across the planet's surface at any given time can be expected to be *sure* to leave some available at the surface a billion years later. Erosion and tectonic forces keep changing the surface.

It must, then, be not only a multiple-record system, but must also be self-replicating, and be given a tendency to seek the surface of the planet.

However, a self-replicating system now compounds the problem of error-transmission, since a defective copy of the message will tend to replicate the error indefinitely.

Somehow, the self-replicating message-carrier device must have an error-detecting-and-rejecting arrangement that will automatically destroy any false copies.

The entire discussion couldn't be printed here, even if I had a magnetic tape recording of it. (Which, I deeply regret, I do not!) The essence of it was that, starting from the proposed problem, these Information Theory and Instrumentation Theory men derived precisely the fundamental mechanism of genetics. And the discussion had gone on for well over an hour before they consciously recognized that they were, in fact, defining genetics!

Dr. Weinstein should have been there! The genetic mechanism is, clearly, precisely such a mechanism as that group sought to define; it has preserved, in *very* multiple record, a precisely accurate message concerning the interaction of carbon dioxide and water—try living on this planet without that information!—and preserved it without error for better than two billion years.

The message is self-replicating, and has a built-in mechanism for eliminating faulty copies. (Any cell with false notions about the interaction of CO_2 and H_2O is immediately self-terminating!)

That the message is recoverable, even after this immense span of time, is being proven by the work of Dr. Weinstein and his associates in the genetic decoding work.

That the message has been preserved accurately—i.e., correctly —is demonstrated by the fact that the living cells are living successfully.

The one factor that wasn't brought out in that bull-session discussion was that it is advantageous to have self-replicating multiple-record devices of many variant types, so that ideally the self-replicating message-carriers should be capable of self-generated adaptations as the planetary surface varies over the megayears. There's no need to make the devices unable to carry additional messages; the requirement was only that The Message should be carried on infallibly.

I think the reason why all terrestrial life has the same basic genetic language—uses the same codon-dictionary—is, simply, because That's The Way This Universe Is. Hydrogen is not cultural; it's universal. The laws of chemistry aren't the private opinions of human beings—or of terrestrial life. There is one, and only one way of making a hydrogen atom. The interactions of CO_2 and H_2O are what they are, and there is no alternative. You *can't* have any different opinions . . . and stay alive in this Universe.

I'm willing to bet that, when we get a chance to study extra-terrestrial life, we'll find that the codon-dictionary is not merely a terrestrial-life dictionary—but the dictionary of biochemistry for all *CHONS*, we might say. CHONS standing for Carbon, Hydrogen, Oxygen, Nitrogen, Sulfur life forms.

Life's business seems to be preserving The Message of Life across gigayears of time, unfailingly, accurately, and always recoverably. The face of a planet isn't stable; it changes beyond recognition in even a few megayears. No structure of matter is stable against the changes of billions of years; even the nuclei of stable atoms are not certainly trustworthy over such a span. Ask any carbon-14 dating expert!

Only the absolute, fundamental laws of the Real Universe are to be considered adequately stable for The Message . . . with the added proviso that if those laws are not, in fact, stable, the self-replicating multiple-copy message eventually transmitted and recovered will then not be accurate, *but will be true!* For the message will have changed to preserve the *meaning*, rather than the *fact!*

Hydrogen isn't cultural, as H. Beam Piper pointed out.

And I'll bet that the genetic codons aren't terrestrial, either.

POLITICS—A NEW LOOK

CONSTITUTION FOR UTOPIA

The standard operating procedure for the Utopia-inventor is to describe his Utopia in terms of how he *wants* it to work. That is, he describes what he considers the goal-ideal of a society should be, and how he thinks that goal ideal will be achieved, in terms of how happy, healthy and wise citizens of Utopia co-operate beautifully to produce wonderful music together. Usually, there's no crime, because, says the author, in so perfect and happy a state no one wants for anything.

There is, however, an astonishing lack of discussion of the legal code on which these Utopias are based—the machinery of the social system is always happily hidden out of sight, and we don't need to look at it, because it works so nicely.

I've seen—and in a college textbook, at that!—a definition of the Socialistic System that read, in essence, "Socialism is a system assuring maximum distribution of the wealth of the society to the productive citizens . . ." That makes things real nice for Socialists; if that is the definition, then, by definition, they're bound to be right! If a system doesn't "assure maximum distribution of the wealth" then, it isn't Socialism, and any system that does achieve that obviously desirable goal is, by definition, a version of Socialism, and see, doesn't that prove Socialism is the ideal system?

It's been standard operating procedure to define Utopias in just such terms—and consider the legal code required to achieve them "a mere detail." Something gross-materialist, anti-idealist, conservative—or whatever opprobrious term happens to be current—people throw up as a deliberate effort to becloud the real, important issues.

Now Utopias always have been in the legitimate field of interest of science fiction; let's try, in readership assembled, rather than in congress assembled, to see what the whole group of some 100,000 readers can come up with in the way of designing a mechanism for a Utopian culture! This editorial is not intended as an Answer to the Question; it's intended to start the ball rolling; Brass Tacks can be the forum. What we're seeking is to pound out a Constitution for Utopia, defining a system that will generate the cultural system we want—*not* a eulogistic rhapsody about how glorious it will be when we get it done.

As a locale, let's consider that the Utopian culture is to be started among the people living in, on, and among the asteroids, about seventy-five years hence. (The locale is not critical, of course; the machinery of government is designed for human beings; what devices they use, where they live, is of secondary consequence.)

To begin with, recognize that we are NOT going to get a culture that is the perfect heart's-desire system of every inhabitant. That is called Heaven.

What we'll have to do is seek an *optimum* culture. It's an engineering problem, and should be approached as such. Many a time an engineer would *like* a material as transparent as glass, as strong and tough as steel, capable of resisting an oxidizing atmosphere at 2500°C., as light as foam plastic, and as cheap as cast iron. *And* as conductive as copper.

The useless engineer is the one who says, "See! They won't give me what I need! It's impossible to solve the problem!" The engineer who *is* an engineer starts figuring the optimum balance of characteristics that will yield not a perfect-ideal, but a thing that will work, and work with a reliability level high enough to be useful for the task at hand.

Now one of the first and broadest questions usually raised is, of course, "What form of government should it be?" Monarchy? Democracy? Oligarchy? Communism?

That question, I suggest, is of no importance whatsoever! Utopia can be a Communism, an Anarchy, or an Absolute Tyranny; the matter is of no real consequence.

My evidence is quite simple: Traditionally, benevolent tyranny is the optimum form of government . . . if you can just assure that the tyrant is, and remains, benevolent. Also, traditionally, both Heaven and Hell are absolute monarchies.

Wise, benevolent, and competent rulers can make *any* form of government utopian—and fools who are benevolent, kind, and gentle, can turn any form of government into Hell. Scoundrels need not apply; scoundrels normally have a reasonable degree of competence, and will, for their own benefit, maintain a higher standard of efficient government than will benevolent fools. Witness the incomparable mare's-nest of the Congo, which has resulted far more from the blundering of fools than machinations of villains. Villains wouldn't have loused things up so completely; nobody can make anything out of the idealistic shemozzle the Congo's become.

Anarchy is government-that-is-no-government. In other words, each individual citizen is his own ruler. Given that all the citizens are wise, benevolent, and competent, anarchy will produce a Utopia. Unfortunately, this requires that each citizen *be in fact*, not simply in his own perfectly sincere convictions, actually wise, benevolent, and competent. The observable norm of human experience is that the incompetent fool will show the highest certainty of his own wise competence, the strongest conviction that his answers can be doubted, questioned, even discussed, only by black-hearted, evil-minded villains who seek to oppose his good, wise intentions.

Given that all the rulers are-in-fact wise, benevolent and competent, Communism works just dandy. The Catholic Church has certainly not opposed the *concept* of Communism—they had it centuries ago in various monastic orders. It's just that the Church objects to the actuality—the legalistic mechanisms—of Russian and Chinese style Communism.

Since it can be pretty fairly shown that *any* form of government—from pure anarchy through absolute tyranny, with every possible shading in between—will yield Utopia *provided the rulers are wise, benevolent, and competent,* the place to start engineering our Utopia is with the method of selecting rulers.

I suggest, in fact, that the only constitution Utopia needs is the method of selecting rulers. England has gotten along rather well for quite a period of time without a formal constitution; if they had a better system of selecting their rulers, no need for a constitution would arise. Wise rulers will change traditional methods of governmental operation when, but only when, the change is warranted. We need not bind future centuries with a code that *now* seems optimum; conditions can change rather drastically. Let us set up a method of selecting wise rulers—and then let their wisdom be fully free to operate. If they choose Tyranny—then it can be assumed that Tyranny is, for that time and situation, the optimum governmental system. With a wise tyrant, it is optimum in war, for instance.

The problem is, was, and continues to be—"How to select the rulers?" Plato talked of "philosopher-kings" . . . but had a little difficulty defining them. The genetic system, based on the unfortunately false proposition "like father, like son" has been tried very widely. Of course, it's heresy to say so in a democracy, but we're members of the Constitutional Convention of the Minor Planetoids, assembled on Ceres, in 2035 A.D., and we can observe that, as a matter of fact, despite the inaccuracy of that father-son idea, the system worked about as well as any other that's been tried. For one thing, it gave England some three hundred years of highly successful government. It's still not good enough—but it's not completely worthless. It must be recognized as having a very real degree of merit. Aristocracy as a system has worked quite well indeed.

Plato's philosopher-king idea runs into the difficulty that, even today, we haven't any battery of tests that can be applied to small children that will, with useful reliability, distinguish the deviant-and-criminal from the deviant-and-genius. Plato's system depended on spotting the youthful philosopher-kings and educating them to the tasks of government; the system won't work, because we can't spot the wise-benevolent.

It gets into further serious difficulty; the way to pass any test is to give the answers the examiner expects. It has nothing whatever to do with giving the *right* answers. Consider a question like "Is the government of the German Third Reich a democracy?" In Germany, in 1941, the answer was, of course, "Ja!" In the rest of the world the answer was different. Incidentally, can anyone give me a standard dictionary definition of "democracy" that does *not*, actually, apply to Hitler's Reich? The *forms* of democracy were there, you know . . . it was just that the rulers operating under those forms were not "wise, benevolent, and competent."

Any formal technique of testing applicants for rulership will have, underlying it, some formal theory of what constitutes "wise, benevolent and competent" . . . which theory rather inevitably turns out to mean "like me."

That's perfectly understandable; the men drawing up the constitution are, of course, playing the role of rulers, temporarily. They feel themselves to be wise, benevolent, and competent . . . or they wouldn't be trying. And, of course, basically everyone feels himself "wise, benevolent, and competent," with the exception of rare moments when, in defense of justice, he has been forced to be malevolent and punish some wrong-doer who unjustly attacked his basic rights. Be it clearly recognized that a homicidal paranoic psychotic, who has just murdered fourteen people, feels deeply that he is wise, benevolent, and competent, and has courageously acted in defense of justice against great odds. They were all persecuting him, and he has simply rebelled against their tyrannies.

Any method of testing, any formal, logical, reasonably worked out and rationally structured technique of selecting those fit to rule . . . will be structured according to the examiners' theories of what "wise, benevolent and competent" means. The use of *any* rationally designed test simply means that the rationality of the test-builders is clamped on the examinees. They pass if they agree with the test-builders.

I suggest, therefore, that the selection of rulers must be based on some nonrational method! Some method which, because it does not involve any formal—or even hidden-postulate!—theory, will not allow any special philosophy of "wise, benevolent and competent" to be clamped on the future rulers.

One possible irrational method would, of course, be selection by random chance. I think it's not necessary to go into details as to the unsuitability of that particular nonrational method.

The method I propose is a nonrational method which, however, practically every logician will immediately claim is the very essence of rationality. It is, of course . . . in an *ex post facto* sense. I suggest a pure, nontheoretical pragmatic test.

Of course, since the ultimate goal of rationality and logic is the mapping of pragmatic reality, there's a strong tendency for logicians to claim that any real, pragmatic test is logical. That's not a valid statement; while it is true that a chain of reasoning is valid if, and only if, it correlates with reality, it is not true that a thing is real only if it correlates with logic.

A pragmatic test is, therefore, a nonrational test. It may be said that "It is rational to use a pragmatic test," but that doesn't make a pragmatic test a rational test. It does not depend on theory—and any rationality does.

The only way we can maintain flexibility of viewpoint in our rulers is to make their selection immune to theoretical determination.

Aristocracy operates on the theory that wise men have wise sons. The theory has value . . . but it isn't sound enough for reliable, long-term use. It gets into trouble because, *theoretically,* the son of the benevolent monarch will be benevolent, but practice turns up a not-quite-drooling idiot every now and then—and the theory of aristocracy can't acknowledge that.

The Communists hold the reasonable sounding proposition that only the politically educated should be allowed to vote. Therefore only Party members, who have been given a thorough education in political theory and practice, are permitted to vote. There's certainly a lot of sound value in that idea; it's not unlike Plato's carefully educated philosopher-kings as rulers. And suffers the same serious flaw; the way to pass an examination is to give the answers the examiner expects. The idea sounds good, but has the intrinsic difficulty that it rigidly perpetuates the political theories of the originators.

A theocracy accepts that only the dedicated priest is fit to rule, because his dedication to things above and beyond this world, and his communion with God, make him uniquely qualified. That system's worked fairly well, now and then.

Robert Heinlein, in his recent novel "Starship Trooper," proposed that only those who accepted the responsibility of defending the nation in the armed forces should have the right to vote. There are very few systems of selecting rulers that have not been tried somewhere, somewhen; that military-responsibility test for rulers has been tried. It works very well . . . so long as the military is run by wise, benevolent and competent instructors. That, however, as I've said, is true of any system of government whatever. In actual practice, the Roman Legions became the effective rulers of Rome during the Empire period—and the results were horrible. Anyone wishing to be Emperor need only bid for it, and if he offered the Legions enough money, they'd murder the current emperor, and install him. One Emperor lasted four days, as I remember it, before someone outbid him.

This, again, is based on the theory that the Legions *should* feel responsible.

Finally, the theory of popular democracy says "Let everyone vote; do no selecting of rulers, and there will be no unjust rulers in power."

That theory is fundamentally false, by ancient and repeated pragmatic test. Maybe it *should* be true, but it isn't. The most deadly dangerous, destructive and degrading of all possible rulers is installed in power when true Popular Democracy gets into power.

The difficulty is this; the old saw that "Power corrupts; absolute power corrupts absolutely," is not quite correct. Power does not corrupt; no matter how great the power a man may hold, he will not become corrupt . . . *if he is not also immune*. It is immunity that corrupts; absolute immunity corrupts absolutely. I need very little power to be a force for unlimited destruction—if I am absolutely immune.

Therein lies the key to that horrible mass-entity known as the Mob. A mob has no organization that can be punished; it is immune.

The members of the mob are immune through anonymity. It has huge physical mass-power; it is immune to the resistance of its victims, and to the opposition of any normal police force. Only an army can disrupt a mob; even so, the mob cannot be punished —called to account and its immunity broken—because it simply disperses, and no one of the ordinary citizens who composed it is the mob, or "belongs to" the mob.

The immunity of the mob can produce a corrupting and degrading effect that utterly appalls those who were swept up in it, afterward. No viciously sadistic affair in the Roman Arena exceeds in corruption and degradation what a modern mob, anywhere in any nation today, including the United States, will do. The mob will do things that not one member of that mob will consider doing.

Immunity, and the sense of immunity, is the deadliest of corrupting influences. It is, in essence, simply the result of cutting off the normal negative feedback, the pain-messages that warn of excesses. Imagine yourself not only blinded, but deprived of all kinesthetic sense, so you could not tell where your limbs were, how hard your muscles were pulling, or whether you were touching anything; you would then be totally immune to external messages. You would certainly tear yourself to pieces in a matter of minutes.

The record of history seems to indicate one fundamental law of civilizations: *The Rulers must always be a minority group,* or the culture will be destroyed.

Note this: under the exact and literal interpretation of democracy, it is perfectly legitimate democracy for a ninety per cent majority to vote that the ten per cent minority be executed by public torture, in a Roman Arena style spectacle.

The advantage of having the Rulers a minority group is that, under those conditions, no group has the deadly feeling of immunity. The Rulers are a minority, and know it, and must rule circumspectly; like the *mahout* driving an elephant, they must rule always with the realization that they rule by sufferance only—not by inalienable right.

The majority, then, knows it is ruled—that it is not immune to punishment, that it is not free to become a mob.

True popular democracy—true rule by the majority—establishes the government of the mob. It was the growing influence of the people of Rome, under the venal and practically inoperative rule of the Legions—the Legions wanted money, not political responsibility; they were fools, rather than villains—that built up to the demand of "Corn and Games!" and the consequences that followed.

A minority group, aware that it is a minority group, is also aware of the problems of other minority groups through direct, personal experience.

Long ago, Machiavelli pointed out that the Prince cannot rule in the face of the active opposition of his people; the Prince must rule circumspectly, for he is a minority.

So whatever system of choosing Rulers we may select for our Utopia—it must be a system that never allows any group to achieve the position that, inevitably, every group wants to achieve—a position of security! The concept of "security" is, in essence, the same as "immunity"; I am secure if I am immune to all attack, or efforts to punish or compel me. The Rulers must never be secure; since they are to have the power of rule, they must not be a majority, so that there will be the ever-present insecurity of the potential threat of the great mass of people. The majority, on the other hand, must never have security from the power of their rulers—or they become a self-destructive mob.

This boils down to the proposition that we want a non-theoretical-rational test for selecting a minority group of people who will be, with high reliability, relatively wise, benevolent, and competent.

The simplest test for this, that does not depend on the rationale and prejudgment of the examiners, is the one the founders of the United States proposed—and which we have rejected. It's quite nontheoretical, and hence has a tendency to be exceedingly irritating to our sense of justice—sense of "what ought to be." The test is simply whether or not a man is competent to manage his own affairs in the real world about him; is he a successful man in the pragmatic terms of economic achievement?

The difference between a crackpot and a genius *is* that a genius makes a profit—that his idea is economically useful, that it returns more in product than it consumes in raw material.

Now it is perfectly true that competence does not guarantee benevolence. But it's also true we have, for this argument, agreed that we're not designing a constitution for Heaven, but for Utopia —an optimum engineering system, not a perfect system. Inasmuch as no one can define "benevolent," we're stuck on that one. But we can say this with pretty fair assurance: a man who consistently injures his associates will not have a successful business for long. A man may *hurt* his associates quite commonly, and be highly successful—provided his hurts are, however painful, essentially beneficial. The good dentist is a simple example. But the man who injures will not be successful for long; the "painless" dentist who is incompetent, and uses lavish anesthesia to cover up his butchery, for instance, doesn't *hurt* his patients, but won't remain in business long.

The founders of this nation proposed that a voter must have five thousand dollars worth of property—a simple economic test, perfectly pragmatic tied with no theoretical strings about how he garnered his five thousand dollars. The equivalent today would be somewhat nearer one hundred thousand dollars.

That particular form of the test is not quite optimum, I think; instead of a capital-owned test, an earned-income test would be wiser, probably. A man can inherit property, without inheriting the good sense of the father who garnered it. But earned-income is a test of *his* competence.

It violates our rational-theoretical sense of justice, because not all men have equal opportunities for education, a start in business, et cetera.

But we're seeking a non-theoretical, non- "just", purely pragmatic test, so that alone would not be an argument against the economic-success test.

Also—to use the dental analogy in another context—if a certain man wants to be a dentist, and has never had the opportunity to study the subject, but sets himself up as a dentist, and wants to work on your teeth . . . why shouldn't he? Is it his fault he never had an opportunity to go to dental school? Why shouldn't he start trying out his own, original ideas on your teeth . . . ?

Are you being unfair to him if you refuse to allow him to practice on you?

And are you being unfair when you refuse to allow a man who never had an opportunity for an adequate education to practice on your nation's affairs? Look, friend—this business of running a nation isn't a game of patty-cake; it's for blood, sweat and tears, you know. It's sad that the guy didn't have all the opportunities he might have . . . but the pragmatic fact is that he didn't, and the fact that he can't make a success of his own private affairs is excellent reason for taking the purely pragmatic, nontheoretical position that that is, in itself, reason for rejecting his vote on national affairs.

There's another side to this pragmatic test, however; neither Abraham Lincoln, George Washington Carver, nor Thomas Edison ever had an adequate opportunity for education. The guy who bellyaches that his failure in life is due to lack of opportunity has to explain away such successful people as those three before he has any right to blame all his misfortunes on the hard, cruel world around. Those three individuals all get the vote, aristocrats, and formal intellectualists to the contrary notwithstanding. One un (formally) educated frontiersman, one Negro born a slave, and one nobody who never got beyond grammar school; three properly qualified Rulers. They made a success of their private affairs; let them have a hand in the nation's affairs. We do not care who their parents were; we need not concern ourselves with their children, for the children will vote only if they, themselves make a success of their own private affairs.

Let's make the Test for Rulers simply that the individual's earned annual income must be in the highest twenty per cent of the population. This automatically makes them a minority group, selected by a pragmatic test. It bars no one, on any theoretical or rationalized grounds whatever; any man who demonstrates that he can handle his private affairs with more than ordinary success is a Voter, a Ruler.

The earned-annual-income figure might be determined by averaging the individual's actual income over the preceding ten per cent of his life, taken to the nearest year. Thus if someone eighteen years old has, for two years, been averaging in the top twenty per cent—he votes. He may be young, but he's obviously abnormally competent. The system also lops off those who are falling into senility. It automatically adjusts to inflation and/or recession.

It isn't perfect; remember we're designing Utopia, not Heaven. We *must not* specify how the income is earned; to do so would put theory-rationalizations back in control. If a man makes fifty thousand dollars a year as a professional gambler—he votes. Anybody who guesses right that consistently has a talent the nation needs.

There may be many teachers, ministers, and the like, who by reason of their dedication to their profession do not make the required income level. If they're competent teachers and ministers, however, they'll have many votes—through their influence on their students or parishioners. If they're incompetent, they will have small influence, and deserve no vote.

The economic test does not guarantee benevolence; it does guarantee more-than-average competence, when so large a number as twenty per cent of the population is included. And while it doesn't guarantee benevolence—it provides a very high probability, for each successful man is being judged-in-action by his neighbors and associates. They would not trade with him, or consult him, if his work were consistently injurious.

There are exceptions, those eternally-puzzling areas of human disagreement between sincerely professed theory, and actual practice. Prostitution is perhaps the clearest example; for all the years of civilized history, prostitution has been condemned. It's been legislated against, and its practitioners scorned . . . by the same population that, through all the years of civilized history have continued to support in action that ancient and dishonored institution.

The people who voted to keep Prohibition on the books were also those who contributed to the high income of bootleggers.

There are many such areas of human ambivalence; no theoretical or rational solution appears to be in sight. The simple fact remains that, by popular vote-in-action, not in theory, prostitution, illegal gambling, and various other socially-denounced institutions continue to win wide popular support.

So . . . Utopia still won't be Heaven. But maybe we can say it will never be a Blue Nose Hell, either!

O.K., friends—now it's your turn!

COLONIALISM

The ideas behind many a science-fiction story have revolved around problems of colonizing other worlds; it might be worth while to take a look at the history of colonization efforts here on Earth. We might get some vague idea of what approach to the problem will *not* work.

So many times, history is disappointing to people, because it doesn't tell them what should be, or can be, done—it's almost entirely a record of tries that failed. Sure that's disappointing— but it can save a lot of future disappointment to take a look at the record of what things not to try again!

Actually, of course, history also includes the record of things that did work . . . but because they did, and we use and accept them, we don't see them as "problems to be solved." Who needs answers to "problems" that are no longer troublesome, huh?

We can start with three general situational possibilities; the planet to be colonized may be uninhabitable by any life form not already possessing a high-level technology, it may already be inhabited by subintelligent life forms, or it may have intelligence already.

The first situation leads normally to a technological station—a research or technical-resource production system—rather than to a "colony" in the normal sense. Antarctica, here on Earth, may have scientific stations, and mining establishments may be installed—but people aren't going to think of Antarctica as "home." The Island of Krakatoa isn't apt to be "home," either, however interesting to vulcanologists and biologists.

What we're really interested in, of course, is the situation involving a planet with intelligent, but subtechnical indigenous life. (The super-technical inhabitants mean that we won't do any colonizing, naturally!)

First, of course, we need a definition of "intelligent inhabitants." This question is about as easily answered as the one "What do you mean . . . 'human'?" As of now, it seems to me that one way to distinguish the merely anthropoid from the humanoid—whether they have tentacles or sixteen legs!—comes down to the question of whether they have a society which acts as a quasi-conscious selective breeding system. If a tribe selects its own young—as early humans did in their "manhood rites" ceremonies—the critical step toward true intelligence has been taken. They have at that point, taken responsibility for their own fate upon themselves—they have started to determine their own destiny, right, wrong or indifferent, none the less the fate they are to have is determined by their own acts.

We'll assume a series of planets having humanoid tribes, which are definitely beyond the beginnings of intelligence, and have already developed their own language, verbal traditions and co-operative cultural systems. There's a range of possibilities in such a situation.

In simplified terms, the Terran-native relationship established can be:

1. The Terrans simply push out the natives, destroying them completely.

2. The Terrans enslave the natives, and force them to work on the Terrans' projects—dig their mines, tend their fields, build their roads, et cetera.

3. The Terrans move in with the natives, start building roads, digging mines, and sowing fields, hiring natives who work side by side with the Terrans.

These are three extremes—three pure-state descriptions. None of them ever has been—or ever can be!—actually applied in its pure form. But each technique has been tried on Earth, and studying the results is most interesting indeed!

System #1, pushing out and destroying the natives, is almost inevitable, do what you, with all good heart and intent, will under certain circumstances. If the cultural-evolutionary gap is too great, it becomes literally impossible to bridge the gap between primitive and highly technical cultural types.

Human beings *evolved*. They didn't suddenly *be* human beings. Adam and Eve is a lovely legend—but there never was a First Man who was a Man in the modern sense, Homo sapiens, who sprang, full-evolved, from some anthropoid mother. Eve's mother was not a hairy-hided, bandy-legged, knuckle-walking gorilloid creature.

Cultures evolve, after the humanoid inventors of culture have themselves evolved; cultures aren't born full-blown either.

Genetics *does* count. It is perfectly true that there is a distribution of talents among individuals in any humanoid group—that, in any humanoid group you will find some individuals brighter than the stupider individuals of a more highly evolved group. But that doesn't mean that the two groups have the same mean distribution!

Studies of the Australian aborigines have shown that when the aborigines encounter the high-level technical culture of the European colonists, their own cultural pattern disintegrates. Even when there is no effort whatever made to break down their primitive culture. The aborigines, however, had a culture so primitive, when white men first came there, that they had not yet evolved the nomad herdsman culture—they were, still, strictly wandering food-gatherers. The economic basis of their culture was still essentially identical with that of gorilla bands. For a period variously estimated as up to fifty thousand years, the aborigines had been isolated from the main stream of human cultural development and pressures.

Curiously, the nearby Maori of New Zealand had a highly evolved Polynesian-type culture, with highly developed governmental systems, and a well-developed technology.

What happened when European colonists moved into the two areas is most interesting. Note that the colonists coming to the two areas were, essentially, of one type—English cultural rebels. Many of the Australians were "colonists-by-request"—people deported for being too much of a headache to the home culture. (Like the Irishman who was deported to Australia by order of the Queen . . . and whom Queen Victoria had to greet in full formal State honors, when he returned twenty-five years later, as the Prime Minister of Australia!) The New Zealand colonists and the Australians were much of the same type, however. Middle-class English, Irish and Scotch, largely.

In Australia, the colonists pushed the aborigines out of their way, destroying the native culture, taking the land, and driving the natives into the desert lands.

The same type of colonists, in New Zealand, developed Colonization Pattern #3—they moved in with the Maoris, worked with them side by side, and have developed New Zealand on a fully co-operative, communal basis.

It's worth considering, at least, that the difference was not in the attitudes of the colonists . . . but the abilities of the natives. The Australian aborigines could not bridge the immense gap between their food-gathering by turning over rocks and logs level, and the technological culture of the Europeans. The Maori could, and very promptly did.

It is of interest in the current United Nations wrangles about "colonialism" and "colonial powers" that neither the Maori nor the Australian aborigines are making any complaints.

The complaints are coming loudest from Africa; the complaints from Asian nations are far less vocal. And, incidentally, the Polynesians generally seem to have little feeling of being victims of "colonialism"—Hawaii might be taken as an example!

Africa represented, almost entirely, a Type #2 colonization program—where the Europeans moved in and enslaved the natives. The Europeans moved in, and sought to work the natives— *not work with them*. In New Zealand, the Europeans worked *with* the Maori—shoulder to shoulder, building a new culture beneficial to both peoples.

In Africa, a very different situation arose. There was the White, who was Noble, and did no manual work, and then there was the Black who was Inferior and did menial jobs. The characteristic of the system is that *there must be no middle class*. When the British in Kenya took over the highlands area, because of its favorable climate and rich soil—it became known as the "White Highlands"—they first drove the natives out, dispossessing them entirely, so that no African was allowed to own land in the White Highlands. But then they found that they had an acute shortage of labor to work their fields. They had fine broad and fertile acres . . . but no labor. The Africans, dispossessed of the best lands, nevertheless had more than enough land in the rest of Kenya, and had settled down to working their own very adequate lands elsewhere. Why, then, should they bother to serve the British land-holders as laborers, when they could work their own lands?

The British solution to this was to limit the amount of land Africans could own arbitrarily. If the African couldn't have lands of their own, then they would have to work the estates of the noble land-holders.

Given a few generations of this system, and you develop a nice, stable Feudalism . . . if you make very sure no Middle Class arises.

Why didn't the land-rich, but labor-poor British of the White Highlands invite the several million land-hungry British farmers, and ex-farmers who'd been crowded into cities, to come to Kenya and help work the vast, rich lands?

Impossible! It would have meant that Whites would have been doing the same kind of menial digging-in-the-Earth that was fit only for Blacks! It would have meant introducing the horrid idea that a man is a Man not because of his skin, or his racial background, but because of what *he* is. It would have meant importing a middle class—creating a mixed-up situation like that in New Zealand!

But . . . the difficulty is that the problem was not all so one-sided. Certainly the British fell into a trap of folly in acting as they did. But, at the same time, the problem was *not* the same as the situation in New Zealand.

The Africans were not culturally evolved as far as the Maori. There was a real problem on both sides; the gap between European and African culture was not as great as that between European and Australian Aborigine—but it wasn't as small as that between European and Polynesian. Polynesians, when the Europeans first arrived, had already worked out a very high level of "constitutional monarchy," with wise, and thoroughly workable democratic procedures for selecting their rulers.

The Africans were, when the Europeans arrived, still in the level of pure ritual-tabu tribalism—with the exception of a Moslem-influenced fringe at the borders of the Sahara, and some of the Zulu tribes in South Africa.

When it's recognized that the same pretty generally homogenous people—the British—showed, under three different conditions, the three extreme responses to the colonist-native problem, it begins to appear fairly probable that the nature of the natives has a great deal to do with the thing! The British in New Zealand responded by working shoulder to shoulder with the Maori; in Australia, they drove out the aborigines, but at no time sought to enslave them to work for them. Yet these same British, in Africa, enslaved the Africans.

It's at least reasonable to raise the question whether or not the Africans were, themselves, responsible for that situation.

The British had gone in in another section of the planet. Now, the African colonization is quite clearly in very dire straits. Australia and New Zealand are certainly healthy and happy and successful. And so is the British-founded North American colonization. By contrast, the Spanish-founded North American colonization achieved nowhere near as high a level of success in the same period.

The United States represents a colony of the Type 1 system— the natives were pushed out and destroyed . . . in major measure.

At this point, I think it's necessary to introduce a new term. "Genocide" has been defined as the murder of a people. I want to suggest something else; "geneocide"—the killing off of a gene, *a particular characteristic* of a people.

In the United States today, the Mohawk people are, very definitely, not killed off! Outside my office window, a new skyscraper is going up—with Mohawk high-steel workers completely dominating the scene. The Mohawk Valley in New York State is still a Mohawk valley, with neat and prosperous, well-managed farms run by Mohawk families.

But the deadly Mohawk raiders, the killers that the colonists of two centuries ago feared and hated, are dead. *That characteristic* of the Mohawk people has been destroyed. The Mohawk high-steel workers have their work, because the Mohawk appears to be blessed with a genetic immunity to fear of heights— which leaves his mind free to pay attention to what he's doing five hundred feet above the ground, instead of battling his internal self-doubts and so missing his step. As one who cannot climb a twenty-foot ladder happily, I sincerely envy the Mohawk.

In other words, in a high-level technical culture, the tendency-to-be-a-raider is a highly contra-survival characteristic, while that genetic immunity to fear of heights is a highly pro-survival characteristic. The interaction of the Mohawk people and the highly successful European cultural system produced a geneocidal effect—but *not* a genocidal effect.

Thus when a high-level culture colonizes an area where Type 3 co-operative interchange is not possible, the natives may be driven out and destroyed—not, however, as a *people,* but *as a genetic type.*

In an individual, the characteristic "homocidal mania" makes co-operation impossible; in rejecting that individual, we are not rejecting him, actually, but the intolerable characteristic that we are unable to separate him from.

If the natives of an area are driven out and destroyed, it's usually because geneocide is necessary; genocide is not intended or wanted.

Type 3 cultural interchange can exist only when there is mutual respect and mutual faith-and-trust. Such interchange with a group such as warrior-raiders is self-evidently impossible. They have homocidal mania as a Way of Life; you can't establish faith-and-trust respect with them.

What are the conditions that do produce a mutual co-operative hybrid cultural system?

When the Puritans first landed here, they learned, and learned rapidly from the local Indians. They adopted the Town Meeting system, the technique of planting corn in hills, with a fish for fertilizer. Both social and technical lessons were freely accepted and learned.

The Indians did not learn anywhere nearly as rapidly from the Europeans. The Indians were happy to teach—to be superior to the stupid immigrants. But they weren't at all willing to be taught. The Mohawks were one of the most advanced Indian tribes; many of them did learn from the "stupid immigrants."

The Maori were willing to teach . . . *and be taught.*

Now you *must* respect a man to learn from him. You do *not* have to respect a man to teach him.

But this doesn't mean that you have to respect a man in all things to learn some things from him. The true test of mutual respect, then, works out to the test of mutual learning-and-teaching. Where that exists, men can work side by side. Where it does not exist, co-operative co-endeavor becomes impossible. And the failure lies with the side that will not learn.

The American Indians were pushed out by the white colonists in North America, because it proved impossible to establish co-endeavor. The Indian would not learn from the White . . . the Indian wanted to be a Noble Savage, which included not working for his living, not grubbing in mines for metals, or slaving in workshops to forge and shape steel, or stewing vile chemical brews to make gunpowder.

For some reason, the Noble Savage lost his homeland as a result. Oh, he liked and happily used the White Man's guns; what he didn't accept was the White Man's hard work that produced those guns.

We might add a new Beatitude: Blessed are the do-it-yourselfers, for they shall inherit the planets!

The Spanish, in the Conquest of America, never got anywhere at all in any of the areas where there was not an already-developed hard-working civilization. The Aztecs, the Mayans, the Incas—these people worked and built their cities. The North American Indians had not reached that level of cultural evolution; the North American Indians could not be enslaved, and the Spanish wanted only slave-worked areas. They were definitely not do-it-yourself addicts.

The Spanish enslaved the less-highly-evolved cultures they encountered . . . and here, the Spanish were playing the Noble Savage! They didn't want to work; they made the Aztecs and the Incas work, they taught the natives to build with new techniques, to mine iron, make steel tools, and establish industry.

Curiously, the Noble Spanish lost their new homelands, as a result.

Recommended reading on the situation in Africa today is Louis E. Lomax's small and very cogent book, "The Reluctant African." Lomax is an American Negro reporter, and a professor of Philosophy; he was in a position to observe data, and to evaluate what he observed, when he went through the length of Africa in 1960. He reports one interesting and revealing incident—of a Ghana representative somewhat sneeringly commenting on the lower standards of living in Liberia and Ethiopia, the two African nations that have been independent for more than a few years. The Liberian representative replied, "We have not had the benefits of colonialism, as you have."

It was the Ghana natives who built the roads, the cities, the telephone exchanges, the power plants . . . but it was Europeans who taught them how, and supplied the capital—which means the tools to make those tools, and the skilled labor to use them properly.

The Africans are in a somewhat peculiar position; they were not willing learners—as were the Maori—nor did they build what they now have themselves. (As the Aztecs and Incas had built even before the Spanish came.)

It rather looks as though whether Colonization System 1, 2, or 3 is installed depends far more on the nature of the natives, than on the determination or choice of the colonists. It was not a British policy to enslave the local natives—it was a Kenya policy, an African-area policy. But the same British acted differently in Australia, North America and New Zealand . . . because the natives were entirely different.

When colonists go into an area—whether it be a continent or an alien planet—where the natives are too far below the cultural level of the colonists, the natives will be pushed aside. Type 1 colonization system results.

When the natives are somewhat higher, they will be enslaved —whether the colonists so choose or not, it appears. And that will, inevitably, result in the destruction of the colony, and a rapid rise in the cultural and living standards of the enslaved natives! In the long run the natives benefit far more than the enslaving colonists!

If the cultural gap between natives and colonists is not too great, the colonists and natives will fall into the third pattern—mutual teaching and learning, and co-endeavor to establish a new, and vigorous hybrid culture. New Zealand, Hawaii, and Alaska all represent that pattern.

At first glance, it may appear that the Eskimo had a very primitive culture indeed; in many respects he certainly did. But the Eskimo was a technologist *par excellence;* in his environment, a highly evolved social pattern wasn't essential to survival—but a highly evolved technology darned well was! The Eskimo has proven to have a fantastic degree of innate mechanical aptitude; a group of Eskimos who had never before seen an outboard engine or any other gasoline engine has been known to disassemble the device completely, and reassemble it in perfect running order. The Eskimo may have been retarded in his social development —but the masterpieces of mechanical engineering the Eskimo achieved demonstrate beyond doubt that they were a highly developed people. They have been delighted to study and learn the White Man's engineering technology—and willing too, to teach the White Man their highly developed skills of arctic survival.

In consequence, the Eskimo, like the Maori, has neither been driven out, nor enslaved. People don't tend to enslave or deport their schoolmates—their fellow-learners.

APRIL 1961

KEEPERISM

I think that if I were the average Vietnamese, I'd want the Communists to hurry up and win the civil war, and get the Americans out.

North Viet Nam is peaceful, has a stable government, clearly understood operational system, and very little confusion. A simple-minded man there is told what the score is, what he has to do, and how he is to do it, and all he has to do is carry it out, and things work out reasonably adequately.

In South Viet Nam, the same simple-minded man doesn't know which end is up, and it wouldn't do him any good to know, because next week some other end will be up. The Saigon government-as-of-today collects some taxes, then the Viet Cong bushwhacks the government troops, takes over, and collects some taxes. The Viet Cong has been collecting tolls for several months on a major highway between Saigon and one of the important northern cities. Theoretically, the highway belongs to the Saigon government, but they can't hold it and the Viet Cong can.

The Buddhists want the Communists to take over, I suspect, partly because the Communists are strongly against religion in the Catholic sense. In most early-citizen-level cultures—Renaissance Europe for instance—"freedom of religion" means that my religion is free to stamp out any and all rivals. Since Buddhism is closer to being a philosophy than a revealed religion, it's more compliant to Communist doctrine, and would, therefore, be less obnoxious to Communist bureaucrats.

The major trouble, however, lies in the fact that the cultural level of Viet Nam's people is not something Americans understand, and the American political philosophy is about as appropriate to them as snowshoes on a gazelle.

We Americans are sort of sold on the idea of Equality for All, and Every Man His Own Philosopher. It doesn't work any too well, even for us—and we represent a cultural evolution that passed through the feuding-petty-states phase some five hundred years ago. (What's happening in southeast Asia today is very similar to what happened in southwest Eurasia—i.e., the European peninsula of Asia—around 1200 to 1600.)

In the first place, the Equalitarian doctrine is probably fantasy, a flat contradiction of known reality. Imposing a fantasy on a human population is always cruel; the further removed from reality the fantasy is, the more vicious the cruelty resulting. The Equalitarian philosophy is somewhat like the Greek legend of the Bed of Procrustes. The tale hath it that Procrustes was a barbarian highwayman who, when he captured some traveling merchant, would entertain his captive at dinner—dining on the best of the victim's supplies—and then put him to bed in Procrustes' guest bed. If the captive was a little too short for the bed, he was stretched to fit; if he was too long for the bed, he was sawed off to fit.

Now if a man were a half-inch too short, it wouldn't be comfortable, but it wouldn't be really unendurable; if he were four or five inches too short, the effect would be very different indeed. Of course, being even one inch too long produced an intolerable result.

The fantasy of Equalitarianism insists that the distribution of characteristics in a human population has a distribution curve like this:

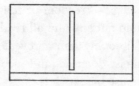

It's flatly-contradictory-to-fact, because every test that biologists, sociologists, psychologists, and other life-sciences researchers have made shows that all biological organisms show a distribution curve approaching this:

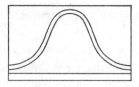

A population on whom the fantasy-equality curve is forcefully imposed has been strapped into a Procrustean bed, and the short stretched to fit, the long sawed down to size, and to hell with what this does to the victims.

One of the worst aspects of this is that the philosophy that all men are equal has the logical corollary that "Since I am a man, and all men are equal, I know what all men are and want."

And naturally, if some men don't want what you want, that simply means that they should be made to, because that's what's good for them, since it's good for you and all men are equal.

Take a look at that second curve, remember that's the one that objective experiment shows exists in *any* biological population *with respect to any measurable characteristic.* This includes measurable psychological characteristics.

To date, we cannot measure many exceedingly important subjective characteristics; therefore it is impossible to prove in any rigorous way that subjective characteristics vary among individuals to the same degree, or in a similar manner. But the weight of evidence strongly suggests that that sort of curve applies equally to such purely subjective phenomena as the capacity for love, the pleasure an individual derives from doing X or avoiding doing Y, et cetera.

Now since only individuals on the higher end of the distribution curve have the talent necessary to achieve effective leadership, effective communication, and effective self-expression against the competition of everyone else trying to get their ideas attended to—the ideas that float around in a culture represent the thinking of *only the high end of the distribution curve.*

How many morons have made their feelings clearly and effectively understood by the general population? About the best they ever achieve is when some demagogue figures out a way to win the moron vote by promising to fulfill some inarticulate but intense desire of the morons. He does so not because it's good for the morons—it generally isn't, of course—but because the resulting moron vote is good for him.

Now one of the greatest desires of the low end of the distribution curve is a deep yearning for stability and security and freedom from having to solve new problems. Freedom from having to generate opinions, make decisions, and think out solutions to problems. He wants a stable situation, with stable, workable and understandable (i.e., memorizable) answers. The answers don't have to be *good;* they simply have to be trustworthy.

The deepest cruelty to this type of man is being stretched on the Procrustean rack that forces him to make his own decisions. "These decisions are killing me!" as the old gag puts it.

An example right here in the United States is the question of "Fair Trade" pricing. Basically, this is a state-law backed guarantee that the customer shall always be forced to pay an inflated price for merchandise, said inflated price being required by law so that an efficient merchant cannot sell the goods at a lower profit margin.

That the merchants would be in favor of such a law *seems* obvious; but why were these "Fair Trade" laws, which assured the consumer that he would be equally gouged by all merchants popular with the consumers? That seems utterly incredible, doesn't it? Yet they were; consumers supported and applauded those laws that assured them that they'd get stuck with the same merchant's profit margin everywhere!

Actually, it wasn't consumer groups that broke down the "Fair Trade" laws—it was merchant groups! The merchants were the ones who worked to have their inflated-profits guarantees removed!

Reason: Under "Fair Trade" laws, a man didn't have to shop around, judge quality and judge reliability of the merchant, or take trouble checking to see if he couldn't find a more efficient merchant who could operate on a lower profit margin. He could go into the first store he saw, say "Gimme one of them!", and walk out assured that he wouldn't find his next door neighbor had the same thing that he'd bought ten or twenty dollars cheaper from a more efficient merchant.

It relieved the consumer of the pressure to use judgment and make decisions. It cost him an extra 50% or so—but he was happy to pay that to be relieved of the problem of deciding.

Successful and efficient merchants get that way by having a high ability to make astute decisions, and accurately evaluated judgments. They have the talent in high degree—and they enjoy using it, as any man enjoys doing what he has a special talent for. The successful merchants wanted to be able to use their talent—and wanted, therefore, to get free of the rigid rules of "Fair Trade" pricing.

People are *not* all equal. You may hold that the man who wants to serve another, have someone else tell him what to do, and when to do it is a vile, slavish, servile, despicable, not-a-real-man type. And so you make a decision for him, and command him to make his own decisions, and not listen to the instructions of wiser men—tell him he must stand up on his own feet, and think for himself. That's what's good for you, isn't it? And all men are equal, so it must be good for him, too, mustn't it? Just because he's a moron who isn't capable of such decisions is no reason why he should be relieved of the responsibility, is it? Make him do it! Lash him with scorn and public rejection and demean him if he tries to find someone he can trust and rely on and be loyal to. You wouldn't like to be that way, so obviously (all men being equal) he shouldn't like it; it isn't good for you, so you know it isn't good for him.

Give him a slogan to be loyal to, instead of a judicious human being. Give him a slogan like "All men are equal!" that he can put his faith in, because slogans are *always* reliable, they *always* work.

Our culture descends partly from the Roman and partly from the Jewish; the Christian philosophy is a hybrid of the two. Like most hybrids, it has some of the hybrid vigor resultant from combining good characteristics from both—and some of the weaknesses resultant from including the worst of each.

One of the worst we got straight from the Romans—who were great organizers, and lousy philosophers. That's the curious concept that The Law Is Infallible. (The Catholic Church has that as a doctrine, explicitly expressed, in terms of Papal Infallibility in matters of Faith.)

A simple, clear, and yet rather subtle example of that doctrine of Legal Infallibility is the fact that if a man is tried and convicted of a crime, and it is later discovered that it was a case of mistaken identity—the wrong man was convicted—the Governor of the State signs a *pardon!*

How can you pardon a man for something he didn't do?

It's the only thing you can do under the hidden-postulate rule that the Law is Infallible. You can't sign a Certificate of Exoneration; that would mean that the Law had been wrong!

A couple centuries ago, the real Sheriff of Nottingham (not the legendary one of Robin Hood fame!) was hanged for murder, because he had executed a tried and convicted criminal, acting on a death warrant that proved to have been improperly made out. Since he had killed a man without *proper* warrant, the exact punctilio of the Law (which is infallible, of course) had been violated, so he was guilty of murder. Q.E.D.—with all the organized logic of the ancient Romans.

This led to the establishment of the Court of The King's Conscience, or Court of Equity, wherein not Law, but Justice reigns.

In "Merchant of Venice," Antonio is saved from losing a pound of flesh when Portia brings a point of legal punctilio to bear; Shylock can have the flesh only if he can take it without a drop of blood being spilled.

The ancient Jewish tradition—which the Moslem tradition maintained, since it didn't go through the Romanization that Christianity did—holds that the law must never be used to destroy a man—i.e., that the purpose of Law is to achieve Justice, not mere logic.

The concept of "A government of Laws, not of Men," is a Christian concept—and means "I want to be ruled by a computer, not by men."

The Jewish-Moslem tradition would never have hung the Sheriff of Nottingham—and if Shylock had been a merchant of Constantinople, instead of Venice, he'd have collected his pound of flesh. Under the Moslem tradition, Antonio would have been guilty of trying to welch on a bet he'd made, simply because he found he was about to lose it.

One result of the Christian doctrine of the Infallibility of the

Law is that we have to have a trick correcting device we call "Mercy." Mercy's function is like that of the Governor's "pardon" for a man proven innocent—to allow a degree of Justice to be achieved when the Law, in strict application, would be irrational.

A recent case, for example: A man was married, and had several children—and one day, disappeared. A decade later he was discovered in another city, married to another woman, established in another business.

Now here is a clear case of bigamy. The Law prescribes penalties for bigamy.

But in this case it was clearly demonstrated that the man had had an accident, and suffered total amnesia; psychiatric examination established that he had no memory whatsoever of his previous life.

This is no problem under the Jewish-Moslem tradition; justice is readily apparent.

Under our rigid Infallible Law doctrine, justice can be achieved only through "pardon," by application of mercy.

Mercy is, in very large measure, a rationalization device by which we achieve a necessary result without admitting the unpleasant truth—that the Law can, indeed, be an ass.

By a simple extension of this principle, not only is Law infallible, but philosophical doctrines, and slogans are endowed with the same mantle of Infallibility. Thus Democracy is Always The Right Answer. And Equality For All Men must be applied everywhere, however many people it ruins.

And Americans go into Southeast Asia, with those very alien cultural concepts driving them and the American people at home demanding that American statesmen apply those Eternal And Infallible Truths. And Southeast Asia has philosophical concepts, and problems, that Americans don't appreciate, and *know* must be wrong, because Americans know the Great Truths.

The term "imperialists" that is so freely applied to Americans by the non-European section of the world is completely false. We aren't; we know it, and the Europeans—who share our cultural traditions—know it.

It's not imperialism—it's a fantastic arrogance! We accept the doctrine of "I am my brother's keeper," and try to live up to it. Only—which the Thoughtless Liberal slogan-quoters overlook!— a "keeper" is someone who cares for *and directs and controls* someone who is incompetent or irresponsible, for that person's own good *as the keeper sees it.*

Works fine, to the great advantage of all, *if the keeper is right.* But it turns into a cruel Procrustean Bed if the keeper happens to be wrong.

Remember that Torquemada, the Spanish Inquisitioner, tortured and dismembered heretics in a great effort to make those poor sinners see their mistake, and confess their sins and shrive their souls. Because he knew that it was far, far more important to prepare for the eternal life to come than to be comfortable and healthy in this life. He was his brother's keeper, striving to rescue those incompetent and irresponsible souls from the danger of eternal damnation.

Procrustes was at least aware that he wasn't helping his victims! His arrogance was as nothing to that of Torquemada.

We Americans are arrogant in Southeast Asia. Our governmental concepts are completely inapplicable; our ideas of what's good for people apply only to people at a particular stage of cultural evolution—ours. What's good for a twenty-year-old genius isn't good for a twenty-year-old moron, and vice versa. What's good for a normal ten year old is a cruel imposition on a normal twenty-year-old. People—and cultures—*are not equal.* They shouldn't be; to think they should, or are, is to believe in an absolute fantasy—a fantasy any living-sciences student can prove completely. The distribution curve applies to *all* biological systems—and a culture is a biological system, whether it's in a Petri dish or a nation.

South Viet Nam quite obviously needs *not* a civilian democracy —which we arrogant Americans have sought to compel. The coups and countercoups would be utterly ridiculous—if they weren't tragic.

Our efforts in the Congo have been accused of "imperialism," and know that charge to be false. What we've missed is that the correct charge is "arrogance" and, perhaps, "Procrusteanism." Or maybe we should call it "Keeperism." "For Their Own Good!" is a vicious concept, when it means stretching the victim to fit a bed that fits us so comfortably.

What would we do if we should land on some alien planet, and find the local native race practices polygamy? Overlook the relevant fact that this race happens to have a two-to-one female-to-male birth ratio, and impose on them the Good Way of monogamy? How shall we do it—kill off half the girl babies at birth, so the birth ratio becomes the Right One? How will our local administrators handle this problem—and satisfy the Folks Back Home who Know What's Right because they've grown up with Infallible Laws? Will those Folks Back Home allow the administrators to maintain that awful-hideous-immoral system of polygamy?

It's a lot easier to see the problems when we transplant them to a visibly-alien environment—but they're fundamentally the problems we're faced with on Earth.

Why is North Viet Nam so much less turbulent than South Viet Nam? "Well of course! They've got a tyrannical military dictatorship of oppressive Communists holding them in suppression!"

Oh? That there's a military dictatorship of Communists is unquestionably true. But as I say—if I were an average Vietnamese, I'd prefer that "suppression" to the tragic-opera coup and countercoup that the South Vietnamese have to try to live with.

Indo-China, under the French, was reasonably integrated and peaceful—because the French supplied the military dictatorship force to keep it that way. It fit the Vietnamese about the way a French *sabot*—the wooden shoe—would fit the barefoot peasants. But it did provide something stable and organized.

Remember that American consumers *wanted* "Fair Trade" laws that guaranteed the merchants would have to gouge them for inflated profits—because they wanted organization that freed them from having to make decisions and work out problems. That American workmen *want* unions, that take care of their problems, even when those unions are run by crooks who gouge them and steal half the union funds.

Under such a system, the people involved know who's gouging

them, and the gougers give them, at least, some stability in return for a tolerable gouge.

Under our idealistic system that we've been imposing on South Viet Nam, we've given them a guarantee of no stability, and imposed on them a you-have-to-make-decisions plan.

And, very simply, *they don't want it.*

Incidentally, it's of interest that the ex-French colonies—and ex-Belgian, who have a very closely allied philosophy—around the world have shown a vastly greater degree of explosive turmoil, when returned to their own devices, than have the ex-British colonies.

It's interesting then to compare the British tradition of domestic self-discipline, of individual responsibility, with French traditions—as manifested, for example, in the Frenchman's approach to taxes. The French government gave up trying to get Frenchmen to be even remotely honest in reporting taxes, and uses a system whereby the tax collector bases the income tax assessed against an individual on the outward manifestations of income. His income tax is based on an estimate of the value of his house, what kind of car(s) he drives, servants employed, his wardrobe, et cetera. What the tax-collector misses on misers, they make up on spendthrifts.

The British have a deeply implanted tradition of individual personal responsibility and law-abiding behavior.

Darned if it doesn't look like they succeeded in transplanting at least some of that in their colonies!

Viet Nam, being an ex-French colony, has a rather low index of respect for the central government and the honesty of bureaucracy—because the citizen considers it his right and sensible duty to cheat where he can. Naturally, he expects the same from the bureaucrat. If caught, he will, of course, pay up graciously; after all, it's the way the game is played.

On top of this is a layer of Communist indoctrination.

Under it is five thousand years of oriental-style feudalism, with virulent local-nationalism.

And we Know The Right Answers for these people?

All evidence indicates that what's needed is a strongly centralized military dictatorship, with a powerful and stable bureaucracy that is rigidly honest. (Enforced by death penalties, not slaps on the wrist and fines.) You don't get that sort of rigid honesty, with enforcement that means enforcement, without a military system. A civilian system won't do it—and the Vietnamese won't have any trust-respect for a civilian system. (They had one for years; they know about those.)

It also requires a powerful, oppressive military dictatorship to make the Montagnards co-operate with the lowland farmers, and the demeaned and rejected fishermen, and the city people. The city-people don't respect those backwoodsmen, or the peasants-on-the-farms, or the smelly fishermen. The fisherman has no trust or respect for the landlubbers of any stripe. And, of course, the peasants know that all non-farmers are out to cheat him of his land, his produce, and his freedom.

These people *aren't Americans, with American traditions and experiences*. They're an alien people, with alien traditions—alien even to each other!—and a lifetime of experiences of a very different kind.

Democracy in Viet Nam? Don't be so stupid! In a culture-conglomerate wherein every group *knows* that there are only two possible situations—either you are Exploited or you are powerful and are an Exploiter? That's not Communist indoctrination—it's their life experience! Democracy? That means, to them, that the gang that gets the most votes has a right to destroy their rivals.

Remember the exact and literal interpretation of Democracy says it's "Rule by the majority." O.K.—and the Nazi majority in Germany passed laws that made killing Jews legal. That's Democracy in Action, bub—and don't forget it! You may forget it, and it may not be what *you* mean by Democracy in Action—but take a wide-open-eye-and-mind look at the Emerging Nations and how they practice Democracy in Action. Particularly the ex-French colonies, with a lower index of individual responsibility. Isn't that definition of Democracy In Action precisely what they've tended to try to put into action?

If you were an average Vietnamese, which would you prefer? Democracy In Action or Communism?

Sure, there are hundreds of alternative choices besides those two. But remember—if you were an average Vietnamese, you wouldn't know about those; those two you've had experience with. The problem isn't American Imperialism.

But the problem of American Keeperism is very real. We know all the answers, we do. That's why we have no troubles of our own at home, and so can tell everybody else how they should be running their affairs. Even if those other people are very widely different from ourselves, because we know they aren't since All Men Are Equal.

JULY 1965

A FINAL EXAMINATION

WE *MUST* STUDY PSI

The essential concept of truth-seeking is that a truth must be accepted, whether it is favorable or unfavorable, desired or dreaded, whether it means riches and happiness, or stark madness. There is, in the concept of the Scientific Method, the fundamental proposition that there are Laws in an ordered Universe; that we must learn those laws—whether we like them or not.

During the last four years, I've been investigating psi; I started the investigation largely because it has been a background element in science fiction, almost from the start. Telepathy has been stock business. E. E. Smith's Lensman series was based primarily on psi—for the Lens itself is, essentially, a psi machine.

With the development of science into engineering proceeding at the pace it has, by 1950 the major developments that science fiction had been forecasting were definitely under engineering —not theoretical—study. It was time for us to move on, if we were to fulfill our function as a frontier literature.

To some extent, science fiction moved on into the social sciences —sociology, anthropology and psychology.

Item: Dr. Rhine originally started his investigation of psi because, as a professional psychologist, he had come to the conclusion that psychology-as-such lacked an essential element. You would have an exceedingly hard time working out biochemistry, if your chemistry hadn't discovered nitrogen, for example. Rhine's studies led him to suspect something about as important as nitrogen to biochemistry was missing from psychology.

Item: Every anthropologist is aware of the important part magic—the psi phenomena under their older name—plays in human cultures.

Item: Every sociologist is aware that you can't make a population behave in a logical manner—cultural superstitions defy logical analysis, logical argument, and logical forces.

I was forced back toward psi, even when science fiction started toward the social sciences.

Since I published the editorial in the February 1956 issue, suggesting running material on psi machines, I have been receiving quantities of information, from hundreds of sources.

I have an advantage that few people have; there are people all over this planet reading Astounding, and for many it evidently has a very personal meaning. I hear from them. I can't answer all; many times no individual letter, or clipping, or reprint sent me has much specific value. But they, taken together, form a sort of Ishihara Color Vision Test phenomenon; no one mass of any one color on the Ishihara Color test disks has any meaning— it's the pattern made of hundreds of individually meaningless dots of pastel color that build the pattern.

I've written a bit about the Hieronymus machine; recently we ran an item about the pipe-locators used by W. F. Marklund of the City of Flint, Michigan. A considerable number of people tried the Hieronymus machine; it proved to be a repeatable experiment in the best scientific sense. Individuals instructed only by the printed word were able to duplicate the phenomena.

But I have not reported even one per cent of the data that has come to my attention. I visited the George de la Warr laboratories when I was in England for the 1957 Science Fiction Convention. I've visited other psi-machine laboratories in Canada, and the United States. I've watched illegal—but beneficial!— medical diagnosis and treatment by psi machine. I've seen records of psi machines used to destroy insect pests in crops.

That, by the way, was a particularly interesting item. The State Department of Agriculture checkers were asked to check the experiment. They did so; standard Department of Agriculture evaluation techniques were used—alternate strips on farms scattered over five counties—some ninety farms in all—were treated, while intervening strips were left untreated as control patches. The checks were made at intervals by Department of Agriculture employees.

At the end of the season, their figures showed that ninety-five per cent of the Japanese Beetles on the test plots had been killed.

And at that point, for the first time, the Department of Agriculture learned that their checks had *not* been made on a new chemical insecticide.

The Department immediately refused to acknowledge the results of their tests. There's no use writing me to ask which state it was, because that state department will deny the check's validity.

The treatment was made by treatment of photographs, at distances ranging from one hundred twenty feet to five hundred miles.

This treatment has, incidentally, shown equally sound evidence of its ability to successfully combat Dutch Elm Disease, and Oak Wilt, which cannot be stopped by any orthodox technique.

Any anthropologist can tell you that the "superstitions" or magical concepts of North American Indians, Australian aborigines, African Negroes, Chilean Indians, the ancient Chinese, the early Norse, the Polynesians, and the Mediterranean peoples contain many identical concepts. These peoples have not had communication for many thousands of years—particularly the Australian aborigines.

Now while I do hold that democracy can go too far, I also hold that democracy has a great, deep value—and the essential of that value might be phrased "You can't fool all the people very long." A completely functionless belief won't fool all the people for tens of thousands of years.

There must be a factor in the Universe itself which those immensely widely scattered peoples have, independently, experienced, and experienced with sufficient regularity to make those concepts remain part of human cultures.

Ours is the only culture that officially denies Magic. And . . . ours does not, by several millennia, qualify as a "very long" culture. The denial of magic is only about three centuries old. You can fool a large percentage of a people for that short a period of time.

The psi machines I've encountered work—and they work on precisely the same ancient laws of Magic that those wide-scattered peoples have, independently, accepted.

I've had that point countered by "Yes, but the common factor is the nature of Man—he wants it to work that way! Therefore peoples everywhere have accepted it. It's human nature, not reality, at work!"

Oh? Then how come human nature evolved that tendency? How come no mutations came along to produce a human variant without that time-effort-energy wasting tendency, huh? Why is it, then, that no human culture, anywhere, has survived even three generations after giving up the interrelated concepts of magic and religion?

If that is, as stated, a fundamental of human nature . . . *why?* We can understand why resistance to disease is a fundamental of human nature—and why a breed that loses that resistance dies out suddenly.

All right—I'll accept that the explanation for the similarity of beliefs among Australian aborigines, Tierra del Fuegians, Africans, Eskimos and Polynesians is due solely to the fundamental similarity of human nature the whole world over.

Why is human nature that way?

And so long as psychologists, anthropologists and sociologists insist "We know it shouldn't be that way," without bothering to study *why all human peoples are that way* . . . why, so long they are apt to miss the fundamentals of the fields they are interested in.

You cannot escape studying Magic, denying that there is any common phenomenon in the Universe, by saying "It's just human nature." Because if you say that, then you are duty-bound to explain why human nature continues to be that way, millennium after millennium. If it is in truth wasted effort, then any people who abandoned magic would have conserved that effort for other things, and would have been able to displace the competing tribes.

Why is Magic fundamental in all human peoples?

I suggest that the answer is "Because there is a set of phenomena in the Universe that requires intelligent entities to have that characteristic."

Like it or not, Marklund in Flint, power company engineers in England, steel plant maintenance engineers in Bethlehem,

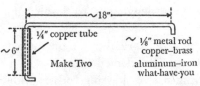

PSIONIC BURIED PIPE LOCATORS

The Pipe Locator drawing above shows the type used by many practicing utilities engineers, the not-inhibited-by-theory types, for locating buried pipes and/or cables. In use, they are held like a two-gun Westerner's two guns, pointing straight ahead, and at about chest height. Walk back and forth across the area under investigation, trying to intersect the line of the hunted pipe. The rods will swing to parallel the line of the pipe as you cross it—either swinging away from each other, or crossing each other. Which reaction turns up seems to depend on the individual, not on the rods.

About eighty per cent of the adults seem to get results; if you don't, let your friends and associates try.

Using them seems to be somewhat like "learning to hear"; anyone with functional ears can hear—but it takes some training to interpret what you hear; e. g., distinguishing the sounds produced by a thrush from those of a robin or blue jay. At first use of the rods, you'll tend to react to all buried conduits; with practice, you'll become more sophisticated in interpretation, and distinguish between, say, water, gas, and sewer pipes.

The operation of these rods is scientifically impossible and is, logically, nonsense. This is extremely interesting, because they work—which, under the rules of the Scientific Method, means that the theory that Science embraces all real phenomena has encountered the fact that it doesn't, and must, therefore, be abandoned. Suggested modification; Science and only Science explains many real phenomena.

Pennsylvania, and in a hundred other places, use dowsing rods to locate underground lines that they are interested in. An engineer with a job to do doesn't give a damn whether the tool he uses is scientifically sound; he does care that it works for him.

And they're very strange tools indeed; for Marklund, the rods locate water pipes, and don't react to buried power cables. For power company engineers, they react faithfully to buried cables, and are not thrown off by buried water, gas, or sewer pipes. For the steel company engineers, they locate buried pipes of any kind; the engineers want to know where the pipes are so that, in driving piling, they won't hit them.

Science has ducked the issue of studying psi very simply; it has denied that there is any phenomenon to study.

In doing so, it is denying a truth—an unpleasant, perhaps disastrous, truth.

The Department of Agriculture I mentioned didn't *continue* their investigations—they denied them.

The engineering use of dowsing rods is widespread today, in the United States, in every state of the Union. There are companies manufacturing dowsing rods such as Marklund uses, and they can be bought from suppliers anywhere in the country.

One company manufacturing them is the Jayco Company, of Birmingham, Michigan; they sell them as the Ayco Pipe Locators.

They are used, strictly at the engineering rule-of-thumb level, by men who find they do a job no other known device will do. They are, simply, pragmatically economical of time and effort. Such men will not waste their time and effort convincing you they work; they have a job to do, and if you don't like their tools, that is, of course, your business, so far as they're concerned.

Science, I can say flatly, with plenty of solid evidence to back it up, is *wrong*. Dowsing rods, used to locate pipes underground, do work. Science is simply, explicitly, wrong in denying the phenomenon.

And this, I propose, is the place that we *must* start studying. We *must*, whether we like it or not—and believe me, from what little studying I've done, we won't like it.

Psi phenomena exist at the same level that emotion, desire, and want do, as far as I can make out. If that's the case, then in studying the psi phenomena, you're studying the level which men, today, hold to be the ultimate level of privacy—Subjective Reality. An understanding of the laws of this level would make it possible to manipulate desire, change attitudes, control emotions.

And that, of course, no man wants possible.

Of all the things Logic and Philosophy and Science have investigated, Emotion, certainly one of the most tremendously important in all human affairs, has been least investigated. Essentially, Science and Logic and Philosophy have agreed on only one thing for sure; "It shouldn't exist! Get rid of it! It just fouls everything beyond hope of straightening out! Stop it—destroy it—stamp it out!"

Psychology, of course, has had to deal with the anathematized stuff. But even psychology seeks to eliminate it from patients; it's an unfortunate, intractable human weakness that must be dealt with.

A logician's attitude toward emotion is startlingly similar to that of a Victorian maiden lady toward Sex. The nasty stuff shouldn't exist, and certainly decent people won't talk about it or investigate it.

Emotion is, essentially, beyond any possibility of logical analysis; it's an individual's reaction to his perception of subjective reality. And so long as "subjective" has the semantic connotation of "not real," logic certainly isn't going to be able to get a real solution to the problem.

I suggest that Subjective Reality bears the same relationship to Objective reality that field-forces do to matter. Field forces are not material; they obey wildly different laws—but they do obey laws.

I suggest that Subjective Reality is a true, inherent level of reality in the Universe. It's no more something exclusively generated by human minds than "organic" chemical compounds were exclusively generated by living organisms. For all men knew, as little as one hundred fifty years ago, the ability to perceive light was a subjective mystery; no known inorganic system had the ability.

It took the development of quantum physics to explain the interaction of electromagnetic radiation and matter sufficiently to make photoelectric cells possible. Eyes, however, had been around for some megayears before that.

To date, no interaction between psi forces and either material or fieldforce phenomena has ever been discovered. Considering the extreme resistance to serious study of psi phenomena, however, that's not exactly surprising. Isaac Newton tried, Oliver Lodge tried—and their efforts in that direction have been hushed up as the indiscretions of two otherwise great men. Probably they didn't have enough data on either psi phenomena or physics when they worked; maybe something more useful could be achieved now.

And we *must* achieve it.

Every human effort to build a dynamically stable civilization—*every* effort, without exception—has foundered on the problem of emotions, desires, and the demogoguery that those uncontrolled wild variables introduce.

And the very best advice Logicians, Philosophers and Scientists have had has been . . . "There shouldn't *be* any such things! Suppress them! Deny them! Do away with them!"

And, every time without exception, they have, instead, done away with the philosophers, logicians, scientists and egg-heads.

You can't control a phenomenon by denying its existence. You can't control it by suppressing it either; suppression simply causes an energy-storage effect that leads to eventual explosive release. If there's a river flowing through a valley where you want to build a city, it's rather futile to simply build a dam to block the river; eventually the dam will be burst by the building pressure, and the city wiped out in the resultant flood.

A phenomenon can be controlled only by acknowledging it, studying it, understanding it, and directing it usefully. Properly handled, that river should be dammed, channeled through turbines, and made to supply the city with light and power.

But emotion is the despair of logicians; it is inherently nonlogical. It's the effort to force it into logic-only channels that causes the explosions that wreck every culture Man has ever built. Uniformly, repeatedly, one hundred per cent of the cases on record.

Evidently what we need is a nonlogical technique of analytical thinking—a method of thinking that is more-than-logical. A not-logical-but-rational technique.

Trouble is, every individual is internally convinced that he's already solved the problem, and is using it right now. And is emotionally willing to work, fight, and, in fact, die for its conclusions. His method of fighting may, for emotional reasons, be limited to a simple absolute refusal, even if he is killed for it—but Ghandi demonstrated that that, too, is a means of destructive fighting.

We must study psi, *because it is the only objectively observable set of phenomena stemming from subjective forces.*

Logic was developed and corrected and forged into a reliable tool because objectively observable phenomena could be used as a check on the validity of logical methods. Logic that didn't correlate with objective phenomena could be eliminated, and logical methods that did work could be proved—in the more ancient meaning of "tested"—by objective experience.

The psi phenomena represent subjective phenomena that can be observed objectively.

When a man uses dowsing rods, the rods don't do anything but act as indicators—the *man* does it. He uses some subjective-level-of-the-universe phenomena; *he* does it, not the rods.

But he does something that isn't scientific, in the truest sense of that statement; the phenomena involved are hyper-scientific. If "natural" and "scientific" are correlated on a one-to-one basis, then what he does is truly supernatural.

Fine; now we know that, and acknowledge that, let's start looking into the nature of the supernatural. It, too, must have laws!

In order to understand psi, we are going to have to develop a totally new kind of analytical thinking; known psi phenomena violate the inverse square law, the distance-law, and every other basic law of Science and Logic. They violate the basic law of Semantics; the map *is* the territory! What is done to the map, is in fact done to the territory—and treating a photograph kills Japanese beetles on a farm five hundred miles away.

That is absolute scientific nonsense—logically impossible!

Good; now inasmuch as it does happen . . . what are the laws of thought, of analytical thinking, that do explain such things? Let us fully understand and agree that it is scientifically impossible, and logically nonsense.

But let us be honest; we do not annihilate the phenomenon by denying the fact that it happens.

As of now, Russia's got us licked at the level of science and logic. We're ahead by reason of progress we made earlier, but our rate of acceleration has dropped way down, while theirs is rising.

In Russia, people truly *desire* science.

In the United States, they do not *desire* science, and do *desire* stability and traditions.

We *must* study psi—even though it will mean development of techniques that will force you, against your will and wish, to desire things that, today, you loathe.

And such psi phenomena as dowsing rods that work for eighty per cent of the people, when used to locate buried pipes, are key facts—objectively observable phenomena—that can lead to breaking the problem of subjective-level reality.

If it was important for the United States to develop the thermonuclear bomb . . . then

We must *study psi!*

JANUARY 1959

DEFINITION

Oxygen An intensely habit-forming accumulative toxic substance. As little as one breath is known to produce a life-long addiction to the gas, which addiction invariably ends in death. In high concentration, it causes death quickly, but even in 20 per cent dilution few survive more than 0.8 century.

NON-ESCAPE LITERATURE

For most of the years I've been editing this magazine, the various non-science fictioneers who have, at one time or another, deigned to investigate this odd-ball phenomenon, have reported on it as a peculiar form of "escape literature." For all of those years, that's intensely irked me. Science fiction, in my opinion, is not, was not, and will not be an escape literature.

I'm beginning to see, though, that the various psychologists, sociologists, litterateurs, et cetera, et al., who have reported on it as an escape literature did have some reason for their statements.

What's finally brought that home to me is the reactions that have followed the launching of Sputnik—and, to a slower time scale, the explosion at Hiroshima.

Most of us in science fiction felt that the introduction of the atomic bomb, and the nuclear power reactors, validating the concepts we had been presenting for years, would bring a rise in the science-fiction field.

It did . . . for a few months. And that was followed by a marked decline, which swept out of the field quite a few magazines that had hastily tried to "get into the act."

The reactions to Sputnik have been more rapid, and, therefore, more readily perceptible and correlatable. There was, again, a sudden rise in interest in science fiction . . . and there is, now, an even more marked dropping of the science-fiction interest. A number of the magazines have been very heavily hit.

I think, now, I know why.

Imagine a man who came across an old, Fifteenth Century *Grimmoire*, full of magical formulas and incantations, and directions for summoning demons. Intrigued and amused by the old superstitions, the pompous ridiculousness of the things the old boys believed, he shows it to a number of friends. They decide it'll be a wonderful stunt for a Halloween party, and go through the ancient rigmarole for summoning a Demon.

And there is the Demon.

Only because it was just a lot of ridiculous flubdubbery, the amateur magicians didn't bother to draw the protective spell of the pentacle. They thought the old boys were kidding . . .

I think the people of the United States thought we were kidding, too. And then . . . there was Sputnik. And we hadn't bothered with the protective spell of the pentacle; all we had was the Pentagon.

I think they thought we were kidding. That nuclear weapons and space flight were amusing ideas to play with . . . nonsense, of course, but amusing nonsense . . .

Apparently, they thought that science fiction *was* an escape literature, and read it as such.

It happens that science fiction's core is just about the only *non*-escape literature available to the general public today. Secret military reports of course are non-escape literature; they discuss satellite stations, bases on the Moon, antigravity devices and the like. They're being discussed in those reports because the men who write them find themselves grimly, terribly, forced to face the woeful reality that things change, and new factors come into action. That there is no security in knowing all the answers to all the known forces . . . because new forces arise.

The essence of "main stream literature" is that There Are Eternal Truths And Nothing Really Changes.

Sure, the Fundamental Things Remain . . . but their value changes. Instincts several hundred million years old remain in Man . . . but they no longer constitute the dominant force in Man. Man still has a sex instinct—but it no longer dominates him so that he is driven to rape any available female. The Ancient Fundamentals make the entire body of mainstream literature—which is, today, almost one hundred per cent purely escape literature. The soft, almost formless, nearly pointless stories found in the mass-circulation magazines are a wonderful retreat from the reality that is somewhat more fundamental than the ones they choose to consider.

It's nicer to say that evolution is based on the survival of the fittest; it's more honest to recognize that it is based on the elimination, the culling out, of the incompetent. That the Universe is not cruel, but it is quite definitely ruthless. You're allowed a weakness . . . if you pay for it with a greater strength, but the payment must be laid on the line, not promised sometime when it's convenient.

Furthermore, we can't buy the Universe; we can't purchase clear title to it. We can only rent space, and the rent on the top-floor space we happen to prefer is simply "achieve more than anyone else in the building does—and that means more than you yourself did last year."

When we fail with that rent, we lose tenure; we join the rest of the culls that Evolution keeps removing.

You don't find anything of that theme in the main-stream literature; it's an uncomfortable lump that wouldn't be nice in an escape literature.

So quite a few people took to reading science fiction and fantasy, because they thought both were fantasy—escape literature about safely, comfortably impossible things like atomic bombs and vampires and orbital satellite rockets and werewolves.

When Hiroshima winked out of existence, some of them were sufficiently disturbed to go back to reading about less unpleasant, more immediate, "realer" things like problems of being fired by the boss for incompetence. But they still thought we were kidding—that it was just bad luck that those weird, and therefore safe, imaginings happened to come almost true.

Besides, it was *our* atomic bomb, wasn't it? So it wasn't quite so bad . . . it was our own, private, well-guarded secret.

But Nature is, of course, a blabbermouth; she'll tell anybody who asks the right questions. The real effect of learning that science fiction wasn't kidding about atomic weapons came when it became manifest that it was *not* our private, vest-pocket secret.

Test Mike was quite disturbing, too. And radioactive fall-out in your own backyard, your own local home dairy delivering milk that made the scintillometers tick off the counts.

Probably nothing is so deeply disturbing as having a nice, safe, fantasy wake up, stretch immense muscles, yawn, and start looking around . . . all on its own, and not controlled by your imagination any more.

The first published discussion of breeder reactors appeared in the pages of this magazine; that was in 1946, and we weren't kidding. The first published descriptions and discussions of thermonuclear bombs appeared simultaneously in this magazine, and its companion magazine, *Air Trails*. That item specified the use of lithium hydride, triggered by uranium, and suggested a twenty-five mile radius of destruction.

So that's a fantasy escape-literature, eh? We were just kidding, huh?

You'll also find a discussion of deuterium-deuterium fusion reaction for power back in 1939, also in this magazine. The basic reasons for using that reaction were outlined; they're the same reasons that underlie the present research for hydrogen-fusion power.

Incidentally, the world will never use uranium, thorium, or plutonium fission power to any major extent. And that's a prediction on which I'm not kidding. The only practical power-reaction for massive use is the deuterium fusion reaction; that, or the lithium-hydrogen reaction. Reason: those two reactions, properly managed, yield helium and energy, and helium is absolutely non-dangerous. Fission products can be tolerated only in small quantities; large quantities cost too much to dispose of. The fuel may be cheap—but the ashes are too damned expensive. Deuterium and lithium are cheaper, and the ashes can be safely dumped right in a man's face.

So we weren't kidding—and the discovery of that fact has lost us some readers. Since Astounding has, throughout its history as a Street & Smith magazine, never pretended it was kidding, and has, for twenty years, been the non-escape literature that seeks to meet the problems of tomorrow in the only possible way —"git them before they git you!"—Astounding has not suffered much. Nearly all of our readers have known right along that science fiction isn't fantasy, and isn't kidding. Hiroshima was an objective confirmation of what we already knew was real; Sputnik again confirmed the theoretical work we had done on the problems of tomorrow. They weren't frightening revelations; we hadn't been kidding ourselves, or anyone else.

But there are a lot of badly frightened people around. Some of those who decided to try science fiction after Sputnik went up must have left even faster than they came. If we weren't kidding when we talked about Sputnik . . . maybe we aren't kidding when we talk about aliens, Out There, who—horror incredible!— might be wiser and more powerful than Man.

It is not my intention to turn to "safe" fantasy—the escape-literature that certainly is becoming more and more popular. Science fiction is not, and never will be a mass-appeal type of material; still, there are some who have the unusual characteristic of being able to enjoy a non-escape literature—who can look at a problem that hasn't slugged them over the head yet, and like thinking about it.

From the consistent, strong shout of "Take it away!" every time Astounding has tried a story verging on the fantasy side, I'm sure this audience doesn't want escape literature.

O.K., friends—stick around. We haven't been kidding—and we aren't going to kid anybody in the future.

Even if they do go on thinking we're kidding when we talk about antigravity, faster-than-light interstellar travel, and some other things we don't have *yet*.

Or . . . at least we don't have them yet *publicly*. But two friends of mine, both professional, recognized scientists, have separately, and circumstantially, reported watching a demonstration of an antigravity device that worked.

At the Los Angeles Science Fiction Convention in September, I stated my personal, present hunch. The first man to reach the Moon *may* get there with a rocket. But the first trips to the other planets will not be made by rockets. Not because rockets couldn't —but because the force field approach will intercept the line of rocket development.

And I'm not kidding on that, either.

WHERE DID EVERYBODY GO?

The data that Mariner II signaled back as it passed Venus last December has been released only gradually—and turns out to be largely confirmation of the completely upsetting fact that Venus has a surface temperature of some 600° to 800°F. It's upsetting, because it shatters nearly all our conceptions of the nature of the planets—and of the probabilities of life on other worlds.

Combined with the recent determination of the nature of Mars' reddish color, and the nature of those polar caps, the Solar System has suddenly become a mighty lonely-looking place. Mars' reddish color, it now appears, is due to the familiar red-brown nitric oxide gas in its thin atmosphere—and the polar caps are solid masses of the white solid form of nitric oxide. It's unnecessary to look for water on Mars, now; if there is any free liquid, the brooks and lakes would be what is now familiarly designated as RFNA —fine for rocket fuels, but Red Fuming Nitric Acid isn't for drinking.

But science fiction has lost more than its Venus colony—at 800°F.? . . . !—and its Mars colony. We just lost the chance for intelligent aliens circling other stars. Because the facts we've now learned force a revision of our most basic conception of What Planets Are Like.

We've been deluded by an especially tricky type of reasoning-trap, that is usually almost impossible to detect until after you've been suckered by it. In this case, it goes "I know what planets are like; I live on one." The stinker in that happens to be that our knowledge relates to a so-far-as-we-know absolutely unique planet, and one that our knowledge to date indicates must be at least extremely unusual in the Universe.

You see, what we've overlooked is the fact that we live on *one component of a binary planet.*

What are the chances of another binary planet like the Earth-Moon system circling another adequately long-lived star at a distance producing a suitable temperature on a clear-atmosphere planet?

Venus has long been described as Earth's twin; with a diameter of 7,500 miles to Earth's 8,000, surface gravity eighty-five per cent of Earth's, at about two thirds Earth's distance from the Sun—it sure looked as though Venus would be very similar to Earth.

The radio astronomers, several years ago, began getting data on the surface conditions on Venus—and the answers were so unbelievable that they were accepted only with the greatest reluctance. That Venus, Earth's twin, should have a temperature that would melt lead was incredible. The fantastically high temperature readings were ascribed to some anomalous radio frequency emission from the planet.

Optical astronomers couldn't penetrate Venus' cloud layer well enough to get even so much as data on the rate of the planet's rotation, let alone get any useful surface detail. The spectroscope, ordinarily able to answer many questions that direct observation couldn't, failed completely on Venus; whatever the planet's rotation rate, it was so slow that the spectroscope couldn't detect it. Whatever the atmosphere of Venus contained, it wasn't anything we could be sure of. Carbon dioxide . . . probably. Water . . . no readable indications. The planet of mystery . . .

Radio astronomers, working at enormously longer wavelengths than those used by optical astronomers, were able to get signals from Venus that most probably did emanate from the actual solid surface, not from the clouds above. But their data came up with insane answers! Earth, if it were at Venus' distance, should have an average temperature of 150°F. That Venus could have a temperature so enormously higher . . .

Repeated checks gave the same answers. And tests for radio frequency spectrum responses due to water vapor—it has spectrum lines in the microwave region, as well as in the "optical" range—gave negative answers.

We've known about the "greenhouse effect"—the ability of an atmosphere to trap solar energy by allowing short-wave visible energy in, but blocking the re-radiation of longer wavelength heat—for a long time. But never in the degree Venus now turns out to have! Venus has a "greenhouse" that could be used for a home pottery kiln, practically—certainly not as either a greenhouse or even a home bake-oven!

The clouds appear to be a solid fifty to seventy-five mile thick layer of the most vicious kind of industrial smog-type components; complex hydrocarbons and assorted mineral acid vapors.

We on Earth here tend to think of nitrogen as an "inert ingredient" in an atmosphere. Completely wrong! Earth now appears to be the only planet in the Solar System on which nitrogen is free in the atmosphere! On the giant planets—Jupiter, Saturn and the rest—nitrogen is linked with hydrogen in ammonia. And to form great mountains of a solid metallic substance that doesn't exist as free metal on Earth—ammonium metal, NH_4. (Under the extreme pressures in the giant planets' atmospheres, $NH_3 + H_2$ is less stable than the solid metallic form, NH_4.)

On Mars, nitrogen is linked up with oxygen in nitric oxide. On Venus, seemingly, nitric oxides are **present** also. (And, incidentally, in the Sun's atmosphere, nitrogen is one of the few elements that can remain in combination even at solar temperatures —that everybody-knows-its-inert element combines with carbon to form cyanogen—CN—can be detected in the solar spectrum.)

Down on the surface of Venus, under the tens of miles of smog, the conditions closely approximate the conditions at the bottoms of Earth's deepest seas in several important respects. The darkness is absolute; there is no light whatever. There is moreover, neither weather nor climate; the immensely thick insulating blanket prevents all temperature fluctuations from day to day—even with Venus weeks-long day—or from year to year. Down there, there is only an unending, searing, black calm.

Earth has jet streams in its atmosphere—stratosphere, to be accurate—which roar around the planet at hundreds of miles an hour, constituting a major heat-distribution mechanism. Venus has jet streams, too—but with the immense depth of atmosphere, and the enormous heat differentials resulting from the very slow rotation, Venus' jet streams apparently achieve wind velocities of thousands of miles an hour.

Those stupendous winds high in Venus' atmosphere do not, however, mean that the surface layers of that atmosphere are disturbed; Earth's jet stream are only a few miles above Earth's surface, yet immediately under a 250-mile-an-hour jet stream there may be the dead calm of a hot summer day.

Venus' atmosphere supports completely opaque clouds some sixty miles above the planet's surface, Mariner II reported. At a fifty mile altitude above Earth, by current definition, a man is legally in space. And certainly it's far beyond aerodynamic flight support!

To be able to support opaque clouds at sixty miles, Venus must have many, many times Earth's atmosphere. If it matches Earth's cloud-layer density at sixty miles, remember that Earth's atmospheric density doubles, approximately, every five miles you go down. If Venus' doubles for each six miles, then Venus must have several hundred times as much atmosphere as Earth.

And this is Earth's "twin planet"?

All the work the geophysicists, cosmologists and astrophysicists have done during the past century must now be massively re-evaluated. In computing the way a planet gains or loses atmosphere, they have, naturally, checked their computations against the facts concerning the available planet—Earth.

It turns out they've been checking their figures against a planetary freak. Venus, nearly exactly Earth's size, retained scores of times as much atmospheric gas—and if anything, Venus is smaller, and we now know it's also very much hotter. Earth's atmosphere should be at least two whole orders of magnitude greater than it is!

Mercury, of course, has no atmosphere; as close to the Sun as it is, and as small as it is—almost exactly three thousand miles in diameter—it couldn't retain gases.

Of the other eight planets, only three have transparent atmospheres—Earth, Mars and Neptune. (Pluto is unknown, but almost certainly clear.) Neptune's is clear because the planet's temperature is so low that nothing but hydrogen, helium and neon remain gaseous; there's nothing to make a condensable vapor at those temperatures. Mars' is clear because of its extreme thinness.

And Earth's is clear because of its extreme thinness.

Every other major planet capable of retaining atmosphere is a clouded-atmosphere, or opaque-atmosphere planet.

Earth's a freak.

In the past, we've guesstimated the probable surface temperature of other planets by supposing Earth were in the orbit of the other planet. In Venus' orbit, Earth would have a temperature of about 150°F. In Mars' orbit, Earth would have a temperature about −40°F. In Jupiter's orbit . . .

And now that we know Earth is in fact a freak, how about trying Venus as the sample—what of Venus-type opaque-atmosphere planets at those different distances? That would make much more sense, since, with the exception of Mars, the others we're interested in *are* opaque-atmosphere worlds!

On the basis of Venus' actual surface temperature, *Jupiter and Saturn both may have a liquid-water surface temperature.*

Recently I had an editorial here on the question of which stars might be expected to have planets capable of supporting life.

All of those remarks now have to be re-evaluated—because it now appears that planets as close to Sol-type stars as Earth and, probably, Mars will *normally* have surface temperatures well above 212°F. Earth would have a surface temperature—if it weren't a freak—above the 372°C. temperature at which water becomes a "permanent gas," i.e., no amount of pressure can liquify it. The life-temperatures zone around a star, in other words, starts for normal, opaque-atmosphere planets, much farther out than Earth, and extends to the region where even an opaque-atmosphere heat-trap can't keep the planet warm.

There is, however, one slight difficulty.

Life evolved on Earth, and we've had a lot of discussion and studies to show that life would, by the nature of things, tend to evolve on any planet having the necessary temperature range.

Sorry . . . try again! On any *freak binary* planet having a clear atmosphere, and also having gravity enough to retain light gases such as the hydrogen necessary for making water.

One of the strange anomalies of life in Earth's oceans is that the Antarctic Sea is by far the most densely populated body of water on Earth. It certainly seems improbable that life should congregate most thickly in that icy cold zone of long, bitter nights.

The reason depends on the fact that life must have three absolute essentials; light, for energy input; fluid for chemical transport medium; and minerals to be transported and interacted.

The ocean deeps have the greatest concentration of minerals; there, there are the minerals needed for abundant life . . . but there is no light, so none of the photosynthetic life forms can get the energy to live, and only a very few scavenger forms live on detritus raining down from the upper levels.

In the tropical waters, where light is brilliantly and regularly available, and the water is warm, which tends to speed biological processes . . . there is so acute a shortage of minerals—particularly phosphorus—that the microscopic plant forms on which the whole life chain of the ocean depends cannot grow.

But in the Antarctic Sea, the deep waters from the ocean floor, heavily laced with minerals, are forced up to the ocean surface —into the zone where light, water, and minerals can be found simultaneously. The sea swarms with life!

An opaque-atmosphere planet presents a not-entirely-dissimilar problem. At the surface of the planet are minerals; at the top of the atmosphere is light energy. But is there any way for the two ever to get together with a usable fluid?

In the case of Venus, we have evidence that there is no water, even in the deep layers of the atmosphere, for even microwave radio astronomy hasn't detected it. But assume a Venus-like planet that did have water vapor.

Now the top cloud layers of Venus have a temperature around sixty degrees below zero F.; the surface has a temperature around eight hundred degrees above zero; there must be a region somewhere in between where water can exist as a liquid.

However, the problem life would encounter is this: at the lighted surface of an opaque-atmosphere planet, the temperature is very low. Ammonia might serve as a life fluid at that level. But the deep levels are much too hot for the cold-level fluid to exist! No one substance would be usable as a fluid both at the lighted top zone, and at the mineral-rich bottom!

There is, of course, always some dust in a planetary atmosphere. How about dust being carried up from the mineralized surface levels to a fluid level far enough up for photosynthesis?

Up through anything from fifty to five thousand miles of opaque atmosphere, you mean? Remember, the bottom of an opaque atmosphere is, by the nature of the processes, calm. Mighty little dust-stirring there, where the dust exists to be stirred. Venus' upper lighted levels may well get more dust-input from micrometeorites falling from space than from stragglers who climbed fifty miles against gravity to reach sunlight.

In Jupiter's case, the outer layers are definitely known to be ammonia clouds, laced with metallic sodium. But the opaque-atmosphere model suggests that Jupiter's surface temperatures must be in the liquid-water range, or perhaps even higher. (If those opaque atmospheres trap solar heat that effectively, they must also block the escape of radioactive heat to a fantastic degree. And the quantity of potassium-40 in the mass of Jupiter would generate *quite* a little heat!)

Jupiter would then be a case of a planet whereon only an ammonia-fluid life form could exist in the photo-active levels—and only a water-fluid life form could exist in the surface layers! And inasmuch as there is strong evidence for free metallic sodium and metallic ammonium in Jupiter's clouds, neither of which can coexist with H_2O, we can drop that problem.

So . . . *can an opaque-atmosphere planet permit the evolution of living forms?*

Evidently life-as-we-know it would be unable to find the three necessities in any place simultaneously.

Now the mass of matter in the Universe is practically pure hydrogen, with some helium, and traces of contamination by heavier elements. Planets, because of their small gravitational fields, lose practically all the gases, and retain only the trace contaminants; Jupiter and Saturn have made out somewhat better, but even they must have lost something like ninety-eight per cent of the original gaseous mass from which their remaining matter was gathered.

The most abundant elements seem to be—after hydrogen and helium, of course—the lighter elements, which are the ones first manufactured in stellar cores, and iron, which is the lowest-energy nucleus and the true ash of stellar thermonuclear reactions. (Energy is *released* in building all elements up to Fe-56; energy is *consumed* in building all elements above Fe-56. U-235 fissions and yields energy because it is far above the Fe-56 least-energy-nucleus structure, and breaking down toward the lighter elements yields energy.)

There are three elements that can't exist in stellar thermonuclear cores—lithium, beryllium and boron have no isotopes that can maintain existence in a thermonuclear core. Deuterium—"heavy hydrogen"—can't remain either. These four react more rapidly, at a lower temperature, than does hydrogen—so they go first and fastest.

The element next after boron is carbon—and carbon, oxygen and nitrogen are the three elements taking part in the "solar Phoenix" reaction, important thermonuclear processes in stellar mechanics. After oxygen comes fluorine—which has a single isotope, F-19, and while it's stable, it doesn't stand up well in a thermonuclear core. Then we get to neon, sodium, magnesium and aluminum.

In the raw material of planets, hydrogen, carbon, nitrogen and oxygen play crucial roles. Hydrogen and oxygen are the most abundant—so far as Solar System indications go!—with nitrogen and carbon less so. Oxygen can combine to form oxides of the rocky types with silicon, magnesium, and aluminum; in addition, hydrogen oxide—water—is, of course, common.

Nitrogen can combine either with oxygen or hydrogen—but at planetary temperatures, neither nitrides of the metals nor the cyanogens seem to be favored.

In Earth's atmosphere, nitric oxides are constantly being formed by solar electron bombardment, UV activity, and by electric sparks—lightning—in the atmosphere. And the biological activities of organisms are greedily consuming every molecule of the combined nitrogen they can get hold of. If if weren't for the biological activities, nitrogen oxides would accumulate in Earth's atmosphere.

In Jupiter's atmosphere, the immense excess of hydrogen swept all the oxygen out of the atmosphere; there, the enormous pressure makes the reaction $N_2 + 3H_2 = 2NH_3$ strongly favored.

On Earth, the free oxygen in the atmosphere tends to favor

strongly the production of carbon dioxide; on Jupiter, the hydrogen excess favors the formation of carbon tetrahydride—methane, CH_4.

In each case, the atmospheres of the planets grow almost solely from the interactions of the four lightest thermonuclear-stable elements, hydrogen, carbon, nitrogen and oxygen.

The thermonuclear probabilities make it very unlikely that any other gases could be important on planets elsewhere in the Universe. Fluorine, the only other first row of the periodic table element, is very low in cosmic abundance. (The helium nucleus of mass number 4 seems to be the stable unit of construction for the lighter elements. Oxygen-16 is four times He^4; carbon-12 is three times, and neon-20 is five times. Fluorine-19 is not favored. Nitrogen-14, halfway between C^{12} and O^{16} and one of the major steps in the "solar Phoenix reaction" is favored.)

Venus' smog-type opaque atmosphere appears to be made up of what might be expected from those interactions. Evidently the planet—somewhat lighter than Earth and nearer the Sun's heat and ionization—lost nearly all its hydrogen while forming. Most of its oxygen combined with rock-forming elements. The remaining hydrogen, nitrogen, carbon, and oxygen assorted themselves into a system partway between the ammonia-methane system of Jupiter, and the nitric-oxide system of the still-lighter planet Mars.

Start with the hydrocarbon-ammonia atmosphere of Jupiter, and reduce the hydrogen content while leaving the other gases fairly constant. The ammonia will go over to nitrogen oxides, the carbon will go from methane, CH_4, to CO and CO_2, as oxygen becomes relatively dominant. The interaction of the resulting mixture of nitrogen and carbon oxides with methane will lead to the production of higher, more complex hydrocarbons and hydrocarbon derivatives. There will be complex aldehydes, alcohols and organic acids, with assorted attached nitro and amine groups.

These reactions will be driven by the high-energy radiation of the Sun—the ultraviolet quanta, impacting electrons and protons, soft X rays, et cetera, reacting on the uppermost layers of the planet's atmosphere.

Our own atmosphere shows traces of nitric oxides from solar bombardment at the uppermost levels, for instance.

Now Venus has so high a surface temperature that there is no usable fluid at the surface. But—suppose Venus had a bit more water, and were moved out to Jupiter's distance. We would then have a curious possibility for a totally new kind of life-system.

That process of radiation-excited reactions between the atmospheric hydrocarbons and nitric oxides will tend to produce fairly complex organic compounds. Radiation-produced amines and radiation-induced acids will combine on contact to form larger and more complex molecules—which will tend to sift downward under gravity.

These complex organic compounds can serve as food for living cells that operate on a fermentation basis! It would be possible, in other words, for a life-system to evolve on an opaque-atmosphere planet, *with no equivalent of plant forms!* The planet's atmosphere itself would serve to fix radiant energy in the form of organic compounds, and the slow trickle of resulting compounds downward to the fluid-mineral supply at the surface would make life possible in total absence of light energy input.

The resultant surface life would *all* be "animal," in the sense of being energy-releasers rather than energy-fixing organisms. Like the living forms at the bottoms of our ocean deeps, the whole system would be dependent on the thin rain of organic detritus from far above. Living in absolute darkness, on very thin rations, they would, in effect, be smog-eating organisms. Their output of carbon dioxide, nitrogen and water would return to the atmosphere, filtering slowly up through the vast blanket of opaque smog, to the reactivation levels where sunlight could act on it.

Life-as-we-know it, with plants and animals in a balanced symbiosis, would not be possible. And the purely accidental radiation-activation of atmospheric components suggested would be immeasurably less efficient than the photosynthetic activities of plants. But still, a thin population of living things could evolve —a population as thin as, or thinner than, that in our ocean deeps.

And this could happen on what we must now recognize as the normal type of planet—the opaque-atmosphere planet.

But . . . could intelligent organisms evolve? Say on Jupiter. Thin as the population might be, with the stupendous size of the planet, there would still be possibilities of millions of entities.

The work on Project Ozma, seeking to contact possible other intelligent races on nearby other-star planets, assumed that any race as intelligent as the human race would, like us, develop and use radio-frequency communication.

We now have serious reason to question that.

On an opaque-atmosphere world, an intelligent race would never see sun, stars or planets; they would have neither weather nor climate.

Human science started with astrology—the science of predicting coming events—seasons—by the stars. It led to the necessity of measurement of angles. Quantitative-measurement is the basis of all our sciences—and they developed largely from astrology and surveying, which developed from the angle-measurement work and geometrical studies astrology induced. Astronomy offers no immediate pragmatic rewards such that a subsistence-level culture would support an observatory and an observer; astrology did. It was most decidedly important to learn how to predict the change of seasons. And then surveying became possible as a sort of unexpected bonus. And then . . .

The dark-world intelligences would not have that stimulus.

On Earth, the Eastern philosophers have tended far more toward the non-quantitative, purely-qualitative fields of subjective phenomena.

If, even on Earth, where there is powerful direct stimulus toward the quantitative measurement sciences, a major portion of the human philosophers have tended toward the qualitative-subjective—what would the dark-worlders do?

Radio techniques are an outgrowth of optics, actually—an extension of electromagnetic theory of light into lower frequencies was the original motivation of Hertz's experiments.

There's evidence that quite different types of possibilities exist, beyond the domain of science we know. Clairvoyants have existed; ESP does occur. Telekinesis has happened.

Suppose that there are planets of Tau Ceti, and Project Ozma's beamed radio signals are quite futile—just as futile as the Tau

Cetans beamed clairvoyance-band transmissions. Never having worked with the electromagnetic spectrum, they don't have the radio-optical gadget we know as TV; they use an equally sophisticated gadget that is a clairvoyance machine. And they know that, obviously, any equally intelligent race anywhere must surely develop clairvoyance transmission equipment.

Would we recognize their civilization if we saw it? Or would they recognize ours if they encountered it?

They've been saying those "flying saucers" are purely illusions. Well—maybe they are. Purely subjective phenomena. Remote clairvoyance pickups, purely subjective devices, transmitted from Jupiter or Tau Ceti VI or . . . ?

But one thing seems rather starkly clear from the data we now have.

The Universe may be full of planets—millions and millions of them. Nice, normal planets . . . like Venus or Mercury or Jupiter.

But Man is going to have a problem. Terra-type planets are binary planets. It takes the contending gravitational fields of two condensing nuclei to strip the gases away from a major planetary body and leave a medium-large planet with a freakishly clear atmosphere.

And we're going to be pretty lonely in the Universe as a result.

Where is everybody?

Hidden under an impenetrable blanket of viciously corrosive smog . . . if they exist at all.

JULY 1963

GOD ISN'T DEMOCRATIC

Over the last few years, successive decisions of the Supreme Court have reduced the areas where religious practices are permitted. Currently, the public schools are no longer permitted to offer prayers to God.

This would, I think, be somewhat startling to the Founding Fathers—and to the peoples who established this nation in pursuit of their own brand of religious freedom. The Puritans—the Quakers—the various religious groups and sects that did a very great deal to build up this nation.

If such a ruling had been handed down by His Majesty's Courts, in the Colonies, in the days of King George III, it could be expected that the American Colonists would have revolted at that point, without waiting for "taxation without representation." The large Irish population in this country came here quite largely as a result of English attempts to induce them to change their religious practices.

The fact that there has been almost no popular rebellion or loud outcry against the Supreme Court decision shows that the attitude of the people on that subject was correctly interpreted by the Court. The American people today do not want God to be so prominent in their lives; the decision of the Court was a popular one—an expression of the feelings of the people of the nation.

Perhaps we can understand the change in attitude toward God and religion in terms of the change of concepts of what is "good" and "the way it should be."

The Colonists who came over here did *not* come to set up a democracy—or any other particular form of political government. They did not revolt against the English King and *then* come over here—they were not motivated by political concepts. The Irish who came over to escape the religious persecution in Ireland were not *politically* motivated in the sense of wanting democracy vs. some other ocracy. They would have been happy to come over to a full absolute monarchy . . . provided the monarchy permitted them religious freedom. Their objection was not that the King of England wanted to be King—but that he wanted to replace the Pope.

It's important to recognize the very real distinction between political and religious motivations—for that very important division is being diluted and washed away in the modern philosophy. Politics is the area of human rule; religion is the area of divine rule.

The major rejection of God in modern societies stems from a simple fundamental: God is not democratic. He violates every basic tenet of Democracy. Naturally such a concept is intolerable in a democratic society.

The basic conception of Deity holds that the Creator is an absolute tyrant, who has such powers of detection and espionage that nothing takes place without His awareness. That His decisions are absolute, unarguable, and—by definition!—always Right and Just. That He has absolute and inescapable power of Life and Death.

In other words, that God is the ultimate in absolute tyrants, with an information system that penetrates everywhere, always, and the ultimate in police power to punish and/or reward.

This is in absolute and violent conflict with the ideals of popular democracy. God is right, even if all the people vote against Him —a violation of the basic postulate of Democracy that the vote of the People determines Right and Wrong, Good and Evil.

The fundamental of theology is that human will, human thought, and human consensus are *not* the ultimate determinant of Right in the Universe. That all men always are and always will be subject to the Will of God.

Now note one factor here very carefully: It is totally unnecessary to raise any question of Faith, or factual reality of the above concepts to be able to analyze the purely logical consequences.

We have two sets of postulates:

1. Democracy holds that the Will of the People is the Supreme and Final determining factor in what is Right, what Should Be Done. That the Will of the People should *direct* executive officers—that the people should not be directed by

their leaders. That any Entity who seeks to oppose or suppress the Will of the People is a—vicious, evil, destructive—tyrant.

2. Religion holds that the Will of God is the Supreme and Absolute determining factor in what is Right, what Should Be Done. That anyone opposing the Will of God will be punished by God, unless he truly mends his ways—and that God, being omniscient, is not going to be deceived.

Now religious freedom, in its true sense, does not deny any of the postulates of religion. Moslem, Christian and Jew—Protestant and Catholic—can all agree on those basics. Religious freedom simply acknowledges that man, not being divine and omniscient, does not know-for-sure *what* the Laws of God actually are. The practice of that degree of humility is something men attained only relatively recently, very bloodily, over many centuries. It amounts to recognizing, finally, that while God's laws are indeed absolute—men's understanding of them isn't.

The religious freedom being sought by the men who founded America was simply that proposition; the right to obey *what they believed* the Absolute Laws of God were.

What we have in America today, however, is something quite different. It doesn't hold simply that no one group can know-for-sure the Absolute Laws of the One God—it holds that if there is a God, there should not be, for He would be an absolute—vicious, evil, destructive—tyrant, since *any* entity seeking to overrule the Will of the People is vicious, evil, and to be rejected.

This attitude is a necessary consequence of the basic postulates of Popular Democracy; the Will of the People is the absolute source of Right, and all tyrants are, *de facto,* evil. Therefore, the Will of God cannot be tolerated, because it would be tyrannical, and evil since it opposed the Will of the People.

Moreover, there are many personal aspects of an acceptance of religion that become acutely discomforting to many people. God has been called "The Great Snoop"; those who would prefer to have their acts and doings very completely private do not find the idea of an all-knowing God at all comfortable.

Then the concept that there are absolute laws that are *not* "just matters of opinion, and my opinion's as good as anyone else's!" doesn't sit well with another type of personality.

God, too, is called The Great Judge—and Democracy has a much kindlier concept; that no one should judge his fellows. This business of a Great Judge who sits in unarguable judgment, as Judge, Jury, and Prosecuting Attorney—complete with built-in and inescapable truth-perception—turns many more away from the idea of such a tyrannical system toward the kindlier ideas of Democracy-without-end.

The churches continue to prosper—but one of the most prosperous I know of is a suburban church where Sunday is the community fashion show and social get-together. Church and Courts alike have recognized the temper of the people, the popular belief that ruling tyrants are inherently evil, to be rejected—an image to be softened. Not a stern, just, all-powerful but merciful King, but a jolly politician type, who recognizes the Will of the People, and does favors for the Right People.

That particular school of theology has been tried by other cultures, other times in other places. It doesn't work. The culture comes apart at the seams—for the essence of that form of "theology" is that there is no hard discipline, no real necessities, in the Universe.

For the revolt is not against God—but against the concepts of discipline, of forces in the Universe greater than human will, and mass opinion. The delusion that popular opinion is the determining force in the Universe, that what The People want is, thereby, Right is a basic tenet of popular democracy as now taught.

It has seemed to me that one of the reasons that so many people dislike Science—find scientists "cold and inhuman"—is that Science consists of studying and recognizing the factors in the Universe that are not subject to popular democracy, are *not* a "matter of opinion," and partake, remarkably, of the characteristics ascribed, by theology, to the Will of God! The Laws of the Universe are quite absolute indeed—and ruthlessly just. Obey them scrupulously, and they work for you; defy them, and you get crushed quite casually, without the slightest bitterness, or anger—or concern.

The scientist, directly concerned with those absolutes, doesn't have the easy, human willingness to give a little—stretch a point for a friend—that the politician understands. He acts almost as rigidly unyielding as an old-time dedicated priest.

Perhaps there is no God after all.

But there is One Universe, and its laws are absolute, unswerving, unyielding, and enforced on us without argument.

The danger to a nation, to a people, is in the idea that the Will of the People can legislate away the necessity for discipline, the necessity of recognizing there are greater and more important things, than human wishes.

Abolishing God may not be quite as simple as the people would like.

It may be that not even the Supreme Court has jurisdiction in that area—that there really is a higher Court that will overrule it.

APRIL 1964